THE VOICE DOCTOR

THE VOICE DOCTOR

The Story of Singing

Professor Arnold Maran

Book Guild Publishing
Sussex, England

First published in Great Britain in 2005 by
The Book Guild Ltd
Pavilion View
19 New Road
Brighton BN1 1UF

Typesetting in Times by
Keyboard Services, Luton, Bedfordshire

Printed in Great Britain by
CPI Bath

A catalogue record for this book is available from the
British Library

ISBN 1 85776 915 5

Contents

Foreword by Dame Anne Evans   vii

Acknowledgements   ix

1   In Space No One Can Hear You Scream   1

2   How Voice is Produced   9

3   The Animal Voice   25

4   The Operatic Voice   31

5   The Music Theatre Voice   53

6   The 'Popular' Voice   63

7   The Earliest Pop Idols   71

8   Will Young Wasn't the First Manufactured Star   79

9   The Classical Pop Stars   91

10   Opera: The Long Road to Big Rewards   99

11   Pop and Rock: The Road of Dreams   117

12   The Injured Voice   125

13   The Lost Voice   133

14   Lifestyle Problems   141

15   Recording Techniques   153

16   Marketing the Voice   163

17   Developments in Voice Technology   179

Index   187

Foreword

The task of speaking may seem simple, but in reality it is one of the most complex physiological functions of the human body. Move from speaking to singing and the complexity becomes even greater.

Arnold Maran explains all this in a witty and simple way. He also provides a history of singing and the inside story of today's world of singers, taking in everything from rock to opera.

For a singer, the most rivetting, and the most important, chapters of the book are probably the ones that describe what can go wrong with the voice. One's vocal cords are only two small muscles and, like the muscles of a dancer or athlete, they must be given the proper treatment if they become damaged or strained. Practically all the singers I know have had a problem with their vocal cords at some point in their careers, though only a few of them might be prepared to admit it. Their reticence is understandable, for most performers are terrified that if managements should find out about their problems they will stop giving them work.

It is high time that this fear is banished for good, because both performers and managements should realise that today very few physical problems affecting the vocal cords are insurmountable, provided the singer takes proper advice and avoids at all costs managements' urgings that he or she should take steroids simply to get through a performance. You do not know what damage such drugs might do to you.

Eight years ago, following the successful removal of a cyst from one of my vocal cords in London, I needed to retrain my voice. I was wondering how to set about it, when a colleague told me about Professor Arnold Maran's Voice Clinic at the Edinburgh Royal Infirmary. I went to see him and he asked me to sing. I sounded like a lady bass. Undaunted, he and his colleague Colin Watson devised for me a series of exercises – vocal physiotherapy – that would raise my voice back to its former position.

Week by week, note by note, I extended my vocal range upwards until, four months later, I returned to the stage to sing Isolde – one of the longest and most taxing roles in the business – in Dresden. I was so nervous that I thought Arnold must have been able to hear my heart thumping, even though he was 800 miles away in Edinburgh. But the voice held – and I never looked back. When eventually I retired from the stage, it was because I wanted to, not because my voice had let me down.

This book provides the answers to so many questions that concern the singer when it comes to vocal health. Read it and take heart.

Dame Anne Evans

Acknowledgements

This book would not have been possible with what I alone knew. I have had enormous help from singers such as Dame Anne Evans, Kathryn Harris, Bruce Ford, Bob Lloyd, Richard Zeller, Morag Mackay, Donald Maxwell and Jane Irwin to mention but a few.

All at Scottish Opera have been most helpful and I must single out, Jenny Slack, Jay Allen, Sir Richard Armstrong and Hector McAndrew.

Athole Still, the most famous agent in the UK, was enormously helpful not only from the business side but in sharing his own knowledge of how the voice worked from the perception he developed when he himself trained as an opera singer.

Rodney Milnes, the doyen of opera critics, shared his lifetime knowledge of opera production and singing with me as did Scotland's foremost teacher, Pat McMahon. Malcolm Martineau, an old friend, was, as ever, willing to lead the blind and deaf through the world of recitals and also to give me insights into the use of the singing voice which were quite unique.

Two voice coaches were also enormously helpful, namely Mary Hammond and Paul Farrington. While they also gave me an insight into the West End musical I remain deeply indebted to Elaine Paige for keeping me right. One day she may be matched by Shona Whyte who showed me how difficult it is to make one's way as a young singer through that particular wood. Carol Kidd, of whom I've been a lifetime fan, told me of the life and style of a top jazz singer, and Tony Williamson instructed me in the world of rock and pop.

Making and selling records was a mystery to me before I was led by the hand through the various processes by the staff of Opera

Rara and my special thanks are reserved for their chairperson, Hettie Ford. I am also grateful to Sandy Matheson, Lorna Brown and the staff of HMV records.

Professor Philip Stell kept me correct from a historical point of view and my medical neurologist colleagues Roger Cull and Bob McMinn corrected my misunderstandings of how the central nervous system controls muscle movement. Dr Andre Phanjoo, a psychiatrist expert in psychosexual problems, informed me how castrati would fare in the world today.

Ian Lennox, who has provided all the diagrams for my surgery books, was persuaded out of retirement for 'one last sketch'.

I must thank Dr Colin Watson and his successor, Martyn Clark, for teaching me physics, maths, acoustics and computing so that I could have a vague idea of the miracles he was creating for the singers in setting up our Voice Clinic and also for his friendship over that period.

My wife Anna must also take her place on this list because it was she who insisted that this book be written before Colin and I shuffled off to another place without our experience and knowledge being made available to others who will follow us.

1

In Space No One Can Hear You Scream

Until this phrase was used in the adverts for the film *Alien* I doubt if anyone had thought about whether you could hear in space or not. After all, we're used to seeing happy astronauts talking to their families or the president on television from within space. But they are in the artificial environment of a spacecraft where they can breathe and hear without helmets on.

If one of them left the spacecraft without a suit and helmet they would perish immediately in a rather spectacular way. But let's say this didn't happen, and they screamed. The film adverts would be correct; no one would hear them.

To make a sound that is heard you have to make the molecules in the air move. Air consists of oxygen, nitrogen and hydrogen packaged into little clumps called molecules. These little balls randomly move about in our environment here on earth, bumping into each other. Because we live under the atmospheric layer and not in space, these molecules are compressed by the upper atmosphere to become closer together. This means that they are able to collide frequently, and so sound is possible.

What is different about space compared to the earth is that there are no molecules under pressure and so no matter how hard you screamed there aren't any molecules to move. So the result is – silence!

If we are going to communicate with each other we have to make sounds that are heard. That needs three things.

First, a sound source, and that's your larynx or voice-box. Second, an environment where there are air molecules that will be moved by the pressure of the sound from your larynx. And third, you need ears so that the moving molecules can arrive somewhere.

Where the voice comes from

You can feel your voice-box or larynx in the middle of your neck. It's a different shape in men than in women. Men have a visible Adam's apple because the 'box' is like the prow of a ship, while the female larynx is more rounded and doesn't stick out as far in the front of the neck. The voice-box lies at the top of the windpipe because it needs to fulfil three functions. The first is to act as a conduit for breathing, the second is to stop what you are swallowing from getting into your lungs, and the third is to produce voice.

Behind the Adam's apple are the vocal cords. They have to close when you swallow for two reasons. The first is to allow the proper pressures to develop so that the top of the gullet can relax and allow food to pass; and the second is to stop the food going down the wrong way.

When you breathe, the vocal cords have to stay apart to allow the air to flow, and when you're running they have to move even further apart because you need more air to flow in and out of the lungs. If the vocal cords come together gently and you exhale, the air passing between them causes them to vibrate and a sound we know as voice is produced. This sound passes into the upper throat and mouth and is altered into speech.

So what's the difference between voice, speech, singing and language?

Voice is the basic sound that is made in the larynx. Speech is the voice broken up by movements of the teeth, tongue, lips and palate. Keep your mouth wide open when you make a sound and all you get is the original sound made by your vocal cords – a prolonged 'aahh' sound. When a baby is born that is all it can do and the sound is interpreted as crying, distress or pleasure. As the baby develops speech in the first year of life it interrupts that flow, first with the lips – 'ma ma' or 'ba ba' – and then with the gums, 'da da'.

Singing is speech used with changes in pitch and rhythm. Language develops as the brain grows. The child learns to coordinate the complex interactions of the teeth, tongue, lips and palate as it learns words. And because, at this stage of its development, it is an expert in learning language, it matters little if these words are English, Urdu or Mandarin. That is why it's so easy for a child to become multilingual.

The way sound is transferred

Somewhere among your older possessions you may find a Newton's cradle – an 'executive' toy once popular as a stress 'buster'. The eight steel balls, suspended by threads from a bar, knock into each other with a 'click', 'click', 'click'. If they don't bring peace they at least provide a good model of how sound is produced.

This is how it works. You pull back the ball on the right and let it go. Click, it hits the second ball. The third, fourth, fifth, sixth and seventh balls apparently stay still and the eighth ball swings out to the left. As it swings back to hit the seventh ball there's another click and the first ball swings out to the right, and so on. The ball at the end swings out because there is nothing to stop it and it holds all the energy developed by all the other balls. That's what happens when you produce a sound from your mouth. The air molecules move, the last molecules have all the energy and provided that there is an ear at the end of the line, that energy goes into the ear and is appreciated as sound.

Sound moves at the same speed no matter what the original source is. Whether it is an atomic bomb or birdsong, sound travels at 1100 feet per second. This is the basis for the childhood game of counting the seconds between the lightning flash and the thunderclap, to find out how far away a thunderstorm is. And it's one of the reasons that crowds can't sing in time with bands at big stadiums, and also why opera singers don't like big theatres with long stages.

High frequency sounds are more efficient than low frequency sounds at shifting air molecules because they hit them faster and more often. This is the basis of the different shapes of musical instruments. Hit a triangle and you've hit a tiny surface area. But the 'ting' is easily heard because the frequency is so high and the wavelength so short.

Stretch a double bass string between two tables and bow it, and you will probably hear very little. The movement of the string is so slow that not enough air particles are moved to hit your eardrum. Put that same string onto a large resonating chamber such as a double bass body and connect it with a bridge, and you can hear it easily, because the large resonance of the instrument's body moves enough molecules to produce sound.

Although it's not quite the same with voices, it's unlikely that

Bryn Terfel would be heard if he was using Lesley Garret's resonating chambers, but if it were the other way around you could still hear the small soprano. In singers, the most important factor in producing a good resonance is how they use the vocal tract, which is the distance between the vocal cords and the lips. But more on that later.

How the ear works

We produce sounds in the air in which we live, but these sounds have to pass into the special fluid in the inner ear in order to stimulate the nerves that take the electrical impulses to our brains for recognition and understanding. Since sound has to go from air to fluid, the ear is designed so that you could literally talk to someone who is under water at the bottom of a swimming pool.

First, we have to amplify the sound that reaches our inner ear. Some of you may be old enough to remember the furore that was caused, especially among owners of parquet floors, when the first stiletto heels were fashionable. Nice new floors became covered in little holes. This was because an eight-stone woman standing on stiletto heels transferred the equivalent of an elephant's weight to the floor. In other words, the transference of a force is greatly increased if it goes from a large area to a small area. This is what happens in the ear.

The eardrum is a relatively big area and is connected by three small bones, acting as levers, to a tiny hole in the inner ear. The inner ear is a tube full of fluid in which there are nerve-endings waiting to transfer information to the brain. The fluid gets an enormous push from the last ear bone and its movement stimulates the appropriate nerve fibres, depending on the frequency of the sound you heard. The codes thus generated are sent to the brain, are decoded and the brain recognises the combination of frequencies and translates them from the memory bank into recognisable words or sounds.

There is no computer known to man that could even come close to this feat.

Why the ear is designed as it is

The human ear is designed to hear the human voice. Everything else is a bonus. Similarly, a bird's hearing mechanism is for communication with other birds and would be useless if applied to humans and vice versa.

Basically, like every other part of the body in all species, anatomical and physiological design is for 'fight and flight', which is the most basic requirement of species survival. The ear has to pick up the very softest noises at the frequency of leaves rustling and twigs snapping and this is around 2.5–3 kilohertz (kHz).

The second requirement of a hearing mechanism is to hear calls for our attention and to receive intelligence in the form of information. We live in a world where most of the noise that surrounds us is low frequency, 0.1–0.3 kHz, which is a long way from the survival sounds in the forest. The information that we need to hear is carried in speech and this has to be heard above the low frequency ambient noise. It is because of the matching design of the hearing and speech mechanisms that we can carry on a conversation with a jet engine going in the background.

Because of these requirements it will not come as a surprise to you to find out that the ear is most sensitive at around the 3 kHz band which is also a band where very little else happens in our lives. It's rather like a dedicated radio frequency which is kept clear for distress signals. In our case, the 3 kHz band is kept free so that we can hear speech.

How the larynx 'fits' our ear

Because of the size of the vocal cords, the sound that they produce has a low pitch. It's about 0.1 kHz in males and roughly double that in females. If that was the only sound that came out then we couldn't hear each other and we wouldn't be able to communicate no matter how loudly we shouted.

But we've just seen that the ear is most sensitive at 25 to 30 times the frequency we produce in the larynx. Whatever your beliefs about the origin of Man, it doesn't seem very clever to have made a sound source that the rest of your species can't hear, especially when everything else in the body is so well matched in form and function. If in fact, that was the end of the evolutionary story then we would look completely different.

When most people talk of their ears they mean the bit that they can see on the side of their head. In most animals the external ears (or pinna) are bigger and more moveable than ours. Animals depend on it to pick up the high frequency sounds that are important for survival. If we had to hear the sound that the vocal cords actually produce then we would need an ear canal that was 10–12 cm longer than our present one and our pinnas would have to be about 3 feet in diameter. That would mean our ears would touch our shoulders and our heads would be a foot wider!

Similarly, just as the ear and head would have to be a totally different shape if we had to hear the sound made by the vocal cords, so too would the larynx have to be different if it were to produce a fundamental sound that the ear could hear in an unmodified fashion. In fact, although our big ears and wide head would make us look odd, the alteration that would be required in the shape of the larynx would be incompatible with life! If the cords had to be of a shape and size to produce a sound of 3 kHz then they would have to be ten times smaller than they actually are, and that would mean that the opening at the top of the windpipe would be so small that we wouldn't be able to breathe.

So what is it that happens to transform our underlying low note to a pitch that allows the ear to hear while not breaching 'design limits'? It's called resonance.

Why we need resonance

Remember the last party you were at. You could hear some people even though they were a long way away from you on the other side of the room – and they weren't shouting. They were *resonating efficiently*. The frequency of their voices was around 3 kHz even though they started like everyone else at around 0.1–0.2 kHz. You may also have spoken to someone who made you feel that you ought to get your hearing tested. Lots of movement of the mouth, but even though you were right next to them you couldn't make out what they were saying. Even if they spoke louder it wasn't much help. They were *resonating inefficiently*. You weren't deaf – they were an inefficient speaker.

6

So what is resonance?

Think of the caves you might have visited. Some made your shout sound better than others. Some had great echos – and some had none. Our 'cave' is the space that the sound produced by the vocal cords enters immediately after we make it. In everyone it consists of three basic parts.

The first part is the upper structure of the larynx, called the 'supraglottis', which is primarily there to fold over the vocal cords and windpipe when you swallow and stop food going down the wrong way. It's basically a tube and it channels the sound into the area at the tongue base. You can change its shape, but not very much, and you do not have a lot of control over this area.

The second part is on a level with the bone that you feel at the top of your neck, just above the Adam's apple. At the back is the relatively fixed back wall of your pharynx but the front, which is the tongue base, can completely alter the shape of this area. Your tongue is shaped like a flexible boomerang. In other words, you can straighten it out or you can increase the curve virtually to a right angle. One arm of the boomerang forms part of the second area and so the way you change the shape is up to you – and depending on how you do it, the sound varies.

Finally, the third part is basically your mouth, and I include the lips in this. This is a 'cave' that you can really alter. Raise or lower the tongue, open or close the mouth, move the palate up or down, pout the lips or pull them back – all of this changes the resonance.

But there has to be something about the original sound that you can use in order to resonate. Play a note on a piano or pluck a string on a guitar – the sound seems to go on for a little after you've played it. Hit a key of a harpsichord and it goes 'clunk' and dies. The difference is that the guitar and piano produce lots of *harmonics* and the harpsichord doesn't. And it's harmonics we need for resonance.

Harmonics

Let's go back to the party and think about what the two types of speakers were doing. They were both vibrating their cords to produce a sound and they both had a surpaglottis, a tongue base and a mouth. But you could hear one and not the other.

And this is why. The 'big' voice was producing a sound signal that had a lot of big amplitude harmonics. We'll discuss the way that happens in a later chapter, but basically it is due to them holding their cords closer together than the soft-voiced person, so that the mucosal wave is strong. If there are lots of large amplitude harmonics then it is easier for the resonating chambers to 'gather' them and concentrate them at around 3 kHz; that makes it easy to hear because that is where the ear is most sensitive. They did this by shaping their supraglottis, pharynx and mouth into a better 'echo chamber' than the quiet-voiced person.

We'll now look at the structures that we were born with that allow us to produce a voice.

2

How Voice is Produced

The voice is not speech, it is not language and it is not song. It's merely the sound made when we vibrate our vocals cords. This sound can be transformed by other structures into speech, language and song but what you hear when you vibrate your vocal cords is the sound you make when you say 'aah'.

The vocal cords lie in the larynx which you can feel as a hard structure half way up your neck. They are exactly at the level of the Adam's apple, are about an inch long and when looked at with an endoscope they resemble two white bands.

The skeleton of the larynx

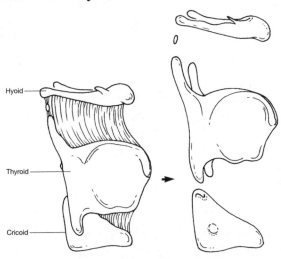

Figure 1   *The skeleton of the larynx*

On top of the windpipe, about an inch above the top of the breastbone, lies a circular ring of cartilage called the cricoid. Attached to it like a visor on a hinge, is the thyroid cartilage. In males it forms a sharp ridge in the neck but in females it is more rounded. This is why males have a more prominent Adam's apple. Above, the thyroid cartilage is attached by a ligament to a bone called the hyoid, which is the one, myth has it, that World War Two Commandos were taught to fracture to cause sudden death!

Sitting on the back rim of the cricoid cartilage are two other cartilages which can swivel in and out; they are called the arytenoid cartilages. The arytenoids are shaped like pyramids with an elongated process in the front and on one side.

Muscles and ligaments of the larynx

The arytenoids are shaped like a three-sided pyramid. The vocal cords are attached to the edge that points forwards and they run forwards to meet at the Adam's apple. Two muscles are attached to the edge that points to the side. One rotates the arytenoid so that the front edges move sideways and open the vocal cords, and the other rotates it in the opposite direction thus closing the cords.

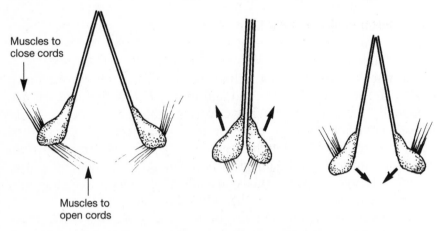

Muscles to
close cords

Muscles to
open cords

Figure 2   *How the arytenoids control opening and closing of the larynx*

Filling the space between the inside of the thyroid cartilage and the vocal ligament is a fairly large mass of muscle called the thyro arytenoid; this is the main muscle of the vocal cord. The part of it

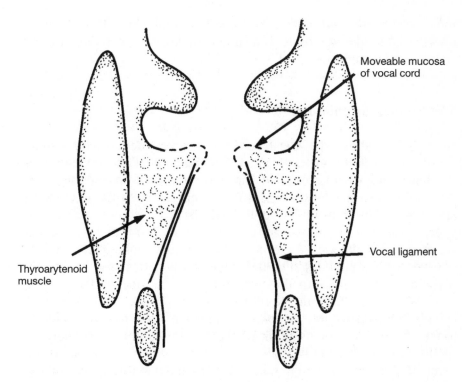

Figure 3   *Cross-section of vocal cords*

that is attached to the vocal ligament has the fibres going in a slightly different direction and is called the vocalis muscle. We'll see what its specialised function is shortly. Covering all of this is a tissue called mucosa, which is not unlike the tissue you see on the inside of your lip. It's smooth, thin, red and moist. Just as the exposed part of your lip has a rather tougher covering than the inside bit, so the mucosa covering the free edge of the vocal cord is of a slightly tougher consistency. This mucosa is not attached firmly to the underlying muscle and ligament; it is separated from them by a layer known as Reinke's space. This space allows the mucosa to slide over the underlying structures like the skin over your knuckles.

The vocal cords thus consist of the vocal ligament, the thyro arytenoid and vocalis muscle and the covering mucosa.

You all know that smoking is bad for you and very few opera singers smoke. The effect on the mucosa or lining of the larynx is quite dramatic. You need light, thin, flexible mucosa to slide over the underlying muscles and vibrate. Smoking changes the tissue of the vocal cords and makes it look like real skin. It is heavier, thicker and harder to vibrate. If a singer smokes they will dramatically shorten their careers.

The Resonating chambers

Immediately above the vocal cords is a three-sided structure made up of the epiglottis in the front, the upper part of the arytenoids at the back and what are called the aryepiglottic folds at the sides. These flow down from the sides of the epiglottis to the tops of the arytenoids. This fan-like structure falls back and covers the larynx every time you swallow, in order to stop food going into the windpipe. The hooded covering that it forms makes sure that all you've swallowed goes into the gullet (which lies just behind the arytenoids) and not into the windpipe. This is one of the reasons that you can't talk while you swallow.

This tube opens into a space bounded by the pharynx and the tongue base. Most of us think of the tongue as ending at the back of the mouth; it actually goes a lot further down the throat to the level of the top bone that you can feel in your throat, just above the Adam's apple.

The three resonating chambers are shown in Figure 4.

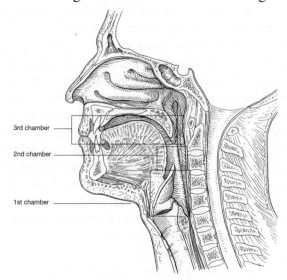

3rd chamber

2nd chamber

1st chamber

Figure 4 *The three resonating chambers*

The supraglottis (the area above the cords) is the first resonating chamber, the pharynx and tongue base area is the second, and the oral cavity and the lips are the third.

We have an infinite number of ways to change the shape of the mouth and thus the resonance. Pout the lips and we lengthen the vocal tract; pull them back across the teeth and we shorten it. Put the tongue flat in the mouth, put it up to touch the palate, place it behind the upper or lower teeth and you get different sounds. Let the soft palate hang down and you get an open sound, tuck it up towards the back of the nose and you get a 'nasal' sound. And every variation of these exists to produce speech, song and tonality.

The lower part of the space passes down into the lungs which are basically the 'bellows' which push a column of air through the cords so that they can vibrate. It might be thought that the large reservoir of air in the lungs represents a resonating chamber but it doesn't. The singer with the big bust or the large chest is using it for breathing, not for resonance.

Muscle control

Muscles don't move of their own accord. You have to make them move and this happens from the brain. You decide to speak and so the vocal cords have to come together so that they can vibrate when you decide to expel air from your lungs. The brain fires impulses down a nerve to the right cord and down a nerve to the left cord, and these are known as the recurrent laryngeal nerves.

On the outside of the visor-shaped thyroid cartilage which is hinged to the cricoid, is another muscle called the cricothyroid muscle. This moves the hinge and dips the thyroid cartilage on the cricoid, thus lengthening the cords. If however the main part of the muscle has a slightly different insertion to the inferior horn of the thyroid cartilage, then rather than a 'tilt' it will be a 'pull forwards'. This muscle is supplied by a branch of the recurrent laryngeal nerves, called the superior laryngeal nerve. We will see later why damage to this tiny nerve may have ended the career of the famous diva, Adele Galli-Curci.

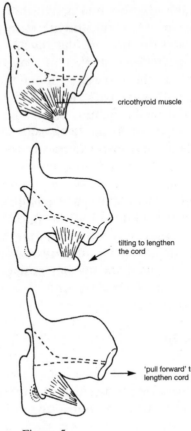

cricothyroid muscle

tilting to lengthen
the cord

'pull forward' to
lengthen cord

Figure 5

Why men and women sound different

There's only a very slight difference in timbre between the voices
of young girls and young boys. The big difference occurs at puberty.
At puberty boys become more muscular than girls. This applies to
all muscle tissue, and is very obvious in the larynx. To accommodate
this, the larynx gets bigger; but it isn't the mere length of the
larynx, as seen in the creation of an Adam's apple, that's important,
it's the weight of muscle. In mathematical terms: frequency =
tension/mass.

We all know large ladies whose laryngeal measurements will be
greater than that of small men, but small men don't all have high
voices and big ladies don't all sound deep. If you try to vibrate

14

any object, it's obvious that a light object will vibrate quicker and more easily than a heavy one. The effect of the change of mass on the frequency is called *impedance*, and as you increase mass, the frequency drops.

Effect of puberty on the voice

At puberty, high testosterone levels create, among other things, bigger and heavier muscles. This occurs in the muscles of the vocal cords and as we saw before, the heavier the vibrating mass, the lower the frequency. The reason boys with breaking voices spend several months singing in between the black and the white notes is that they are developing heavier thyro arytenoid muscles unequally. If the mass on each side is unequal then there is not sufficient neural compensation and the voice sounds as if it is 'cracking' because the frequency frequently changes almost mid-word.

At puberty, girls' voices also drop, but only a little. Their thyroid cartilages also change shape – not to the sharp prominence of the male Adam's apple, but to a more rounded shape. This makes it rather difficult for the arytenoid cartilages to fully meet at the back and so there is always some inefficiency due to air escape in the female voice. This gives it an attractive 'breathy' quality.

The voice is a major problem for transsexuals. While a prominent Adam's apple can be whittled down surgically, there is no way of reducing muscle mass in the hope of raising the pitch of the voice. While speech therapy can train them to speak with a breathy, higher voice, they are let down when not concentrating, laughing or shouting.

Effect of ageing on the voice

Some women, in the premenstrual phase, retain fluid in Reinke's space. This has the effect of slightly deepening the voice and it was not uncommon 50 years ago for sopranos in European opera houses to have specified days off each month.

As people get older, most male voices rise and female voices drop, a problem that not infrequently is very upsetting. The male voice tends to rise because of muscle wasting and loss of mass with a consequent change in the impedance. Females tend to collect fluid in Reinke's space which has the opposite effect, especially noticeable on the telephone.

How the vocal cords produce a sound

If you kept your vocal cords apart and exhaled, you'd only hear the hiss of escaping breath. Interrupt that column of air by making speech shapes with your tongue, teeth and lips, and you'd be whispering. Put the cords together and do the same – now you hear voiced speech.

So, quite simply, blowing air through vocal cords that lie together makes the sound we know as voice. Make the sound of laughter – 'ha, ha, ha, ha, ha'. Each 'ha' was made with the vocal cords together. In the silences between the 'ha's' the cords were either open or you weren't blowing any air up from the lungs. Now do a long 'ha'. This time you'll continue making a noise and the only limiting factor will be either your lungs running out of air or, less likely, your vocal cords getting tired from being held in one position for so long.

The vocal cords weigh about the same as a quail's egg. The vibrations that make up the male voice happen at about 100 times a second, and in a female 200 times a second. It would be virtually impossible to move two structures the weight of the vocal cords that quickly. So if the vocal cords don't vibrate, what does?

It's the thin lining on the surface of the vocal cords, the mucosa that I previously likened to the lip tissue. What happens is this. You put the vocal cords together with a tiny chink between them (colour plate 1). You blow air through this gap from the lungs. The mucosa is vibrated because it can slide up and down the underlying muscle and is light enough to do so at over 100 times a second (colour plate 2).

You can imitate this action with your lips. Purse them together and blow hard through them. This is in fact what brass players do to play their instruments. If you're not a brass player you might not make a pleasing sound but you ought to produce something like a 'raspberry'. A trumpet player could play a tune just using the lips, going up by tightening and lengthening the lips, and going down by narrowing and slackening the lips. You probably can't do that because you haven't practised it. But you have practised using your vocal cords. In fact you've been 'blowing raspberries' and changing pitch virtually since the day you were born.

Maybe you couldn't blow a raspberry with your lips. Try again, but this time make sure that they are moist. More success this time? If so, it illustrates the second important thing about producing a sound from the larynx: the surface of the cords have to be wet.

Remember the last time you lost your voice due to a cold? Well, that was due to general throat dryness that accompanies a cold and which also gives you the sore throat. There was almost certainly nothing 'wrong' with your vocal cords when you lost your voice other than the fact that when the mucosa vibrated it didn't 'click'. You can demonstrate this to yourself by putting your thumb and index finger at your ear and separating them. No sound? Try again; this time with slightly moist fingers – and you'll hear a 'click' as the fingers separate.

How the mucosa vibrates

When we think of vibration we think of surfaces meeting together from side to side. For many years, using unsophisticated older equipment, that is what we thought the vocal cords did – move against each other, side to side. Wrong! The edges of the vocal cords are not like the edges of a knife. They are much blunter than that and are in fact several millimetres deep. Try to imagine them as a couple of pieces of Brie, with the 'nose' cut off.

The mucosa at the bottom of the wedges meets first, and closure of the rest of the mucosa covering the cut nose of the Brie follows until there is complete closure; the air flow then pushes the closed mucosa apart and the cycle begins again. Imitate it with your palms. Put them together with the fingers facing away from you. That's the situation of the mucosa at full closure. Now slowly open the palms from below upwards, and when the thumbs separate, put the lower edges together again – and so the cycle starts again. It's basically what a bird's wing does.

This happens over 100 times a second but in the lab we can display these cycles one by one and apply various measurements to diagnosis and treatment. We illustrate what this looks like with a laryngogram, which is a very valuable tool for the voice doctor. It lets him know how the vocal cords are functioning and very often shows a voice coach which areas to work on. It is an easy and painless investigation to perform and only involves the singer holding a couple of plates on the neck skin overlying the larynx.

Figure 6 shows a schematic laryngogram. The first upgoing line is the mucosa closing. In a singer we like to see that line as vertical

17

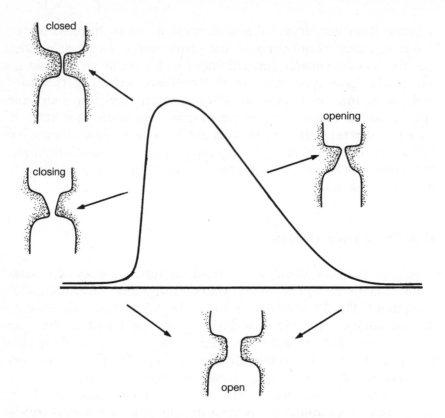

Figure 6   *A laryngogram showing the position of the cords at different points in the cycle*

as possible because quick closure produces better and bigger harmonics. As the line reaches the top it means that there is complete closure of the mucosa and as the mucosa separates, so the line goes down again but more slowly. At the bottom there is a pause till the next cycle starts. Again it matters little for speaking but in a singer we like to see this segment as short as possible because the more contact, the more power.

There is a huge difference between the laryngogram produced by a singer and a non singer. In a singer the cords are held closer together which means that the collision of the lower end of the wedge occurs quicker and earlier. Not faster, so that the frequency rises, but earlier, so that the airflow is interrupted quicker. This results in bigger harmonic signals being produced. In a non-singer the cords meet much more slowly with the result that the harmonics are weak resulting in little resonance (colour plate 3).

18

The second thing that the singer, as opposed to the non-singer, does is to make the surfaces of the wedge come together quicker. This has two effects. The first is that the column of air coming up from the lungs is interrupted more frequently and so there is less air wastage, and the second is that the build-up of air under the closed cords is greater and the next 'puff' has greater pressure. In this way the professional singer makes the most of the manoeuvring of the air column to produce a sound that we recognise as the 'professional' voice. It is a bright, powerful voice that projects a long way effortlessly, and it is stable.

What the laryngeal muscles do

When you speak or sing, your laryngeal muscles keep the cords together, keep an equal tension on each side and set up a stable platform on which the mucosal wave can function. If you want to raise the pitch of the voice you lengthen the vocal cords, and if you want to speak with a lower pitch then you shorten them. You alter the length of the vocal cords by lengthening and shortening the thyro arytenoid muscle and also by tilting the thyroid cartilage on the cricoid by contracting the cricothyroid muscle which is on the outside of the larynx. As important as mere lengthening and shortening of muscle is the alteration of tension. Shortening a muscle without altering the tension within it would just lead to the creation of a useless floppy lump. Similarly you couldn't lengthen a muscle without an initial release of tension and a resetting of it at the new length.

The control you require to do this is fantastic. I am sure that you didn't realise you were capable of such muscle control! Think back on what I said about boys with breaking voices. The voice cracks for a few months as the muscle changes shape, not because of differential weights but because the individual can't produce exactly equal tensions in both cords at the same time.

Think of your eyes. When you look to the side you see (I hope), one object. That is because your right eye moves exactly the correct distance to balance your left eye so that only one image of whatever you were looking at hits the retina. That's phenomenal. The eyes actually move different distances so that the object you're looking at forms one image and not two.

Imagine trying to get exactly the same tension in each of your biceps – or even more improbably, each of your buttocks. The simple answer is that you could never accomplish that because the control mechanisms that are necessary for it don't exist in bigger muscles, only in smaller ones that are required to perform fine movements.

Muscle control

All muscle is made up of hundreds or thousands of muscle fibres, depending on the size. They are all under the control of the central nervous system, which comprises the brain and the nerves that flow from there to the muscles of the body. If you don't need to use a particular muscle for fine movement, for example the thigh muscles, then one branch of the main nerve will supply a few hundred muscle fibres. In that way, when the nerve is activated, a lot of muscle moves at one time and you are well on the road to getting the powerful movement that this type of muscle produces.

On the other hand, if you want to pick up a small object from the surface of a table, then you need finely adjusted and very accurate pressure between the fingers in order to accomplish very precise movement. If you used too much power you would break the object and if you were not accurate with grasping and lifting it then you would knock it off the table. Muscles that have to perform fine and accurate movement such as the eye muscles, the finger muscles and the larynx muscles are innervated in a different way. Instead of a nerve supplying several hundred muscle fibres, in the larynx for example, one nerve supplies four muscle fibres. It must be obvious therefore that the more control that is needed of a muscle, the more intensive must be its nerve supply.

Each group of muscle fibres and its supplying nerve is called a *motor unit*. There are two important reasons why muscle is arranged into groups of motor units.

The first is so that the brain can regulate the force that you apply to any particular movement. All muscle is always in some sort of state of contraction. It's called *muscle tone*. If all muscles were permanently relaxed we'd fall about like rag dolls because we couldn't keep our skeleton steady. So when you want to move a muscle you have to add some more power (i.e. more motor units) to those that are already working.

20

The feedback mechanism is called the *myotatic reflex* and is the fundamentally important factor in any movement. If you want to do anything with any muscle, the brain first of all has to know how many motor units are active. The first thing that happens therefore is that a nerve fires onto a special receptor in the muscle to get a check on this. Once this information is passed back to the spinal cord a second nerve fires on the number of motor units the brain reckons is required for the task.

An important part of this reflex arc is the fibre that goes to the muscle with the opposite action (called the *antagonist*), to tell it to relax. There wouldn't be much point in trying to lift something by bending your forearm if the triceps, the big muscle at the back of the upper arm was at the same time trying to straighten the arm! In Chapter 13 we'll see how failure of this fibre to function can cause a singer to lose their voice permanently.

This reflex is bypassed if you are in danger. Let's say that someone stuck a pin into you. The brain would sense danger and the prime consideration would be to get you out of that danger. So you jump with a mass muscle movement. It's not a fine movement, there's no coordination about it, but it's effective for what the brain deems to be required at that particular moment. But if you want to pick a coin off a table or if you wish to sing a soft scale, then you need just the right amount of muscle activity to accomplish what you want to do. And that is muscle control.

The second reason that muscles are arranged into motor units is so that they don't get tired. If you use all of the motor units in any muscle at one time then you have only a finite time before that muscle gets tired and gives up. The best example of this is watching weightlifters in competition. They use all of their motor units at one time in their lifting muscles, for obvious reasons. If however they can't lift the weight first time, the muscles give up because there are no spare motor units to bring into action.

What the rest of us do when we are performing a prolonged muscle activity such as cycling, is to use some motor units for a time, rest them and use others, and then go back to employing some of the first lot – and so on. Eventually all of the motor units will tire because the recovery period might take longer and longer but generally we can keep going in a muscle activity much longer than if we'd used all our motor units for a huge burst of activity right at the start of what we were doing.

What the lungs do

The lungs are rather like balloons that have to be blown up. Their natural position is 'collapsed', and if they remained like this you would not be able to live because no oxygen would get to the blood.

They are shaped like tilted prisms. The thin upper end lies behind the collar bones at the base of the neck and the base of the prism is under the ribs you can feel in your back. In other words there is more lung tissue in the lower part of the chest than the upper part.

The ribs have two functions. First, they protect the lungs from external trauma because a collapsed lung is life threatening. Secondly, they act as an attachment for the muscles that lie between each pair of ribs; when these muscles contract the ribs move outwards rather like a bucket handle and the large lung base fills with air. At this point the diaphragm helps by moving downwards displacing however much fat you have in your belly or chest wall. It's an effort, as fat ladies who are said to end operas, will attest to.

As your lungs are filling with air, your diaphragm is pushed down and your rib cage is tilted outwards. The speed that you breathe out is governed by how you let these two structures act. If you're running 400 metres then they move pretty quickly because your blood is crying out for more oxygen. If however you're singing a slow soulful aria then you want the air to come out as evenly as possible. When you want to sing loud, the air comes out quicker and when you want it soft, you let it come out slower.

We'll look at traditional methods of teaching singing later in this book and we'll note the huge emphasis that is put on the use of the diaphragm in breathing. Sorry, but the diaphragm is totally a muscle of breathing *in*, not out. The important thing is the muscles in the chest wall. What stops you holding your breath for a long time. The cigarettes? The lack of training? The build up of carbon dioxide? No, none of the above. It's the proprioceptors, that is the 'adjustors', of the muscles of the chest wall getting tired. You can train them to last longer. Servicemen in the Special Boat Service can work underwater for up to five minutes. But that hasn't got a lot to do with singing so we'll move on.

The rate that air comes out of the lungs depends on the opening it has to go through. There's an analogy here between the vocal cords of a singer and the lips of a flute player. A professional flute player, with a tight embouchure (a tiny tight opening between the lips), will be able to play continuously for very much longer than an amateur whose slack lips allow air to be wasted all over the place. Similarly with singers. If you belt the noise out, then you've got to take lots of breaths, and if you've got to do a long Wagnerian line then the cords have to function with great control and accuracy.

3

The Animal Voice

Although this is a book about the human voice, let's take a backwards trip and see how and why voice evolved.

Animals have voice boxes in much the same place as we do, namely at the top of the lungs and in front of the swallowing apparatus. Like us they have to stop food going down the wrong way, but unlike us, mainly because of their less developed brain, they don't need to communicate so meaningfully or so frequently. Also, eating and smelling the scent of predators is more important than communication.

Survival is the most important aim of most animal species. A grazing animal on the African plain has to smell the lion predator a mile away and so has to be able to breathe to pull in scents while eating. In most animals therefore the epiglottis is much bigger than in humans, and separates the air from the food passages.

The main reason for animals to have voice is to attract mates, to dissuade predators and in some species to claim territory. Different species live different sorts of lives but apart from the bird the basic structure is the same as ours.

Let's look at that champion of song first – the bird.

How and why birds sing

Birds have a voice-box in a different place from ours. It's much nearer the lungs and is in fact beyond the point at which the windpipe enters the lungs. When you consider the complexity of birdsong then it will not come as a surprise that they have not one, but two, sources of voice production.

25

They sing for three reasons. The first is to claim their territory, the second is to let possible predators know that they are fit and well and not for being eaten today thank you, and the third is to attract mates. Some live above the tree line, some live in trees, some on ponds and some at an even lower level. So the song has to be adjusted to carry to their theatre and their audience.

The larynx of a bird is called a syrinx. The basic structure is a membrane at each branch of the windpipe as they enter the lungs. The ability to sing a duet 'within itself' allows a bird to produce a much greater number of meaningful sounds than humans.

How are birds able to sing non-stop for what appears to be minutes on end without pausing for a breath? If we did this we would have to take in an enormous breath and let it out very slowly – and even then we couldn't match the skill of a bird. This is because a bird actually takes a series of 'mini-breaths' which are synchronised for each syllable they sing. The canary can in fact take 30 mini-breaths per second. The nearest analogy to human behaviour is the 'rebreathing' techniques that jazz saxophone players use to play a solo without a break.

The repertoire of many birds is greater than that of a concert pianist or violinist. The nightingale, for example, can sing almost 300 different love songs. The chaffinch, who has fewer songs, may sing his half a million times in a season. The brown thrasher has over 2,000 songs in its repetoire but the male may never repeat exactly the same sequence of elements twice during the course of his lifetime.

Wherever they live, birds have a way of letting themselves be heard even when they are not seen. In the open, sound travels best a metre or so above the vegetation. Birds living at this level can sing continuously. In the forest, sound bounces off trees and is absorbed by the leaves. So here, frequent brief signals are heard best. Many small birds therefore sing on elevated perches high in the vegetation to minimise interference from ground and foliage. In Britain, the skylark solves the problem by soaring high, singing, hovering and then plummeting down almost vertically.

The best time of day to hear birdsong is at dawn. This is the best time for sound to travel because there is usually less wind and less ambient noise or sound disturbance. Sounds broadcast at dawn can be 20 times as effective as sounds broadcast at midday. In the evening, the few birds who sing, like the nightingale, may dominate the air for hours.

But what are they saying? It's almost always the males who are singing. They are declaring that they own territory and they are usually singing for other males. These territorial songs carry over a long distance and convey detailed information about the location and identity of the singer. When they pause in their song it is to listen for a response and to identify where the rival is and how far off.

When they are trying to attract females into their territory, male birds become more operatic; they sing longer and more complex songs, but the females in general do not respond. They will go around listening to several males before making their choice. The winner will usually be the male with the most complex songs and the largest repertoire.

In some species the female will join the male in songs in defence of the territory. Birds such as ravens will sing alternate duets because this helps them to maintain contact. Each one of a pair learns the other's song and when one partner is away or out of sight, the other will often call with its mate's individual call to make contact and get it to return.

How dogs bark

Dogs basically bark to warn or to greet. They have a larynx that is almost an exact copy of the human larynx and before anti-vivisectionists slowed things down, experiments in laryngeal surgery were all done on dogs.

The big difference between humans and dogs however is that dogs do not have a vocal ligament in their vocal cords. They thus have a 'floppier' structure. They can't fixate the vocal cords in the same way as humans, so when a blast of air comes up from the lungs the cords cannot maintain a stable platform and so the mucosal wave can only occur briefly. If a dog sets his vocal cords together and blows air through them the sound is a whine. They can do this for several seconds and when experiments were done on dogs to find the best way of rebuilding a larynx after excision for cancer, all the measurements were done on the quality and effectiveness of this whine.

When a dog barks it does the same as Louis Armstrong did when he sang – it brings the false vocal cords together and the rough sound of a bark (or a Louis voice) is produced. The sound of a repeated bark is due to short blasts of air going through a tight larynx with false vocal cord vibration.

As we saw in the section on the pubertal voice, the heavier the cord, the lower the voice. So when big dogs with more tissue in their vocal mechanism than small dogs blow air through the closed larynx the sound is deeper. Big dogs sound fierce and little dogs sound 'yappy'. However, when either big or small dogs blow air through a tightly closed larynx then the sound emanates from the true vocal cords and because their tension and stiffness is high then the whine is not much different between small and large dogs.

Neither dogs nor cats, either big or small, use voice for mating or marking territory. This is done by scent glands which are better understood by the animals themselves rather than us!

How cats purr

No one knows how cats purr. We know that they purr when they are content. It was thought that they were so relaxed that they opened their vocal cords and allowed the upper part of the larynx, the first resonating chamber or supraglottis, to come together and vibrate when the air passed through. This would have seemed a reasonable explanation but the sound goes on when the cat is breathing in as well as out. This also would be acceptable provided that there was a break in the purr as the cat changed mode from breathing in to breathing out. This doesn't happen. So basically no one knows how cats purr.

Why giraffes are dumb

As I was preparing this book I talked to many eminent veterinary surgeons hoping to find the answer to some of these animal communication questions, but I was disappointed. Vets obviously have more major things to consider than how animals actually produce voice.

To be fair however, the why is more important than the how. Giraffes have long since interested me, however. You may recall that I mentioned that the nerves to the vocal cords, called respectively the left and the right recurrent laryngeal nerves, have different courses. They both come from the vagus nerve which travels from the brain, through the base of the skull, through the chest to the abdomen, supplying almost everything of any importance on the way. The recurrent laryngeal nerves comes off the vagus as branches. The one on the right comes off as the vagus passes close by the larynx in the neck and so is fairly short. The left one however does not break away from the vagus until it enters the chest and for unfathomable reasons of embryology, it passes round a ligament near the heart and runs back up the neck to the vocal cords.

In humans, this 'reverse' journey is only a few centimetres. Let's consider what that means. When you, or any of your animal cousins, want to make a noise, the brain tells the vocal cords to come together. Our nerve fibres within the left recurrent laryngeal nerve are slightly thinner than those on the right, so the message travels a little quicker on the left than the right, in order that both messages arrive at exactly the same time at the vocal cords. If they didn't, we would warble like a pubertal boy every time we started speaking on a new breath.

Thus, even though the nerves are of different lengths and messages that start in the brain have to end up in the vocal cords at the same time there must be a difference in conduction time. This is accomplished very accurately in the human by a minor difference in nerve fibre size and orientation. In the giraffe however the difference in length is about a metre. There is a difference in nerve fibre size between the left and right recurrent laryngeal nerves but it is almost an evolutionary 'step too far'. This is probably why giraffes don't say very much. They have a larynx that if instructed correctly could make a noise but basically they say nothing. But do they need to?

They are unique in the animal kingdom. Not only can they smell predators, but also they can see them from a great distance. A sudden movement at their height will be seen by the whole herd or family, and so danger can be averted. And their unique size and passive demeanour leads to uncomplicated mating without the need to call for a mate like a bird.

4

The Operatic Voice

Although the majority of people like popular music as opposed to opera, it would be generally conceded that the way operatic singers use the voice is the ultimate in perfection. They all do the same physical things to produce the 'operatic sound' but it is the indefinable quality of beauty that separates the best from the very best.

I've often been asked if, by looking at someone's vocal cords, I can tell if they either are or will be a good singer. The answer is always a resounding 'No'. I'll go even further. If I saw a photo of Luciano Pavarotti's vocal cords, and one of David Beckhams, I would probably not be able to say which was which! Similarly I would be willing to wager that if a sports physiotherapist was shown David Beckham's right leg – let's say through a screen so they didn't know who was on the other end – and the right leg of a similar sized footballer in one of the lower leagues, I would doubt whether they could identify which was which.

So why can't I tell much from just looking at the vocal cords? There are a number of reasons. Firstly all I can see is the white gleaming surface. I can't see what the muscles are like, nor can I tell how good their control is just by looking at their covering. The laryngeal muscles are so small that you can't define one from another under their covering of mucosa. In the same way, the wonderfully controlled lip muscles of trumpeters like Chet Baker or Wynton Marsalis lie under the mucosa of the lips. But from the outside, they just look like normal lips. You might think that since Michael Portillo has bigger lips than either, then he ought to be a good trumpeter, or an even better one. He may well be but his records aren't seen in the shops! So the message that I hope is getting across is that with small muscles like the

31

lips, the larynx and the fingers, it's not the size that counts – it's the control.

Types of voice

Discovering one's voice may take many years. At the extremes it's easy. The higher sopranos, basses and basso profundos have an anatomical structure that fits them to their particular sound and it is rare for them to change. At the interface of higher baritone and tenor, and dramatic soprano and mezzo, it is not infrequent for a singer to switch. While the overriding reason will be vocal, there are also commercial aspects to be taken into account. There are fewer tenors and mezzos than baritones or sopranos, so work is possibly easier to obtain. Placido Domingo started his professional life as a baritone but switched to tenor roles but his voice still has the characteristic of a high baritone.

Female singers are classed as soprano, mezzo-soprano and contralto There is however no dramatic difference in their range and they form part of a continuum (colour plate 4).

The soprano's lowest note will be middle C, but the contralto's lowest will be only four notes lower, with the mezzo in between. The very highest soprano will hit a G above top C, but most sopranos will do a top C comfortably and a contralto will get to within two or three notes of this.

Male voices are categorised as tenor, baritone or bass. The lowest note for a bass is about the F below bottom C and the tenor should manage the C above middle C. Male and female voices overlap and in fact every singer, both male and female, from the lowest bass to the highest soprano can sing the F above middle C, but with a totally different quality and using a totally different technique.

What's important is the quality within the ranges. For example, the soprano will not sound good in her lowest three or four notes nor will the contralto at the upper end of her range. Similarly, tenors have difficulty at the bottom of their range while basses have problems at the top. So the operatic parts are, with a few notable exceptions, written so that the voice chosen by the composer sits comfortably within the scope of the music.

What decides voice type

There are essentially four things that decide a voice type. These are the muscle mass of the vocal cord, the amount of hyaluronic acid in the submucosa, the length of the vocal tract (which is essentially the neck length), and finally the inherent elasticity of the vocal ligament.

The heavier the cord, the lower the frequency that results from any vibration. Basically that is why men have lower voices than women. But within this general rule, there are intra-gender variations. Some people will have a little more muscle than others and this decides their most comfortable range. Thus, some women will be more comfortable as mezzos and some men as baritones.

Similarly, hyaluronic acid is present in the submucosa of the larynx in everyone. It is a chemical that collects and attracts water. The more you have, the more fluid is in your cords and potentially, the deeper the voice. Females have three times less than the average male and within each gender some have more than others. Basso profundos have it by the bucketful and coloraturas will have very little. It is essentially an adjuvant to the basic weight of the muscle, and if a singer has more then they will be able to sing lower, and if very little, then they will reach the highest point of their range.

Hyaluronic acid is more of a problem as women get older. After the menopause, many women have heavier vocal cords due to the deposition of hyaluronic acid, which has an enormous ability to draw in more fluid. The voice thus drops and professional singers may find it harder to get to the top of the range with the ease that they formerly used to.

Since females sing higher, their fundamental frequency is at a pitch that does not produce a lot of harmonics. To achieve projection at 3 kHz they have to make the most of what they do produce. The most important part of resonance is the length of the resonating cavity, which is made up of the supraglottis, the pharynx, the oral cavity and the lips. It's measured from the vocal cords to the lips and it should be around 17 cm in the male and 15 cm in the female. A male produces more harmonics, has a much longer resonating cavity and has less difficulty in projecting the voice.

The way that a female singer alters the length of her resonating tract is mainly by using the tongue and the lips. You can't do a lot about the length of your neck or the size of your oral cavity,

33

but when millimetres are important in a short tract, you can do a lot with the front of the mouth. So the female singer tunes her resonances with her lips, her teeth and the wideness of her mouth opening. This is why you usually see female singers open their mouth far wider than males, and why they often pull back their lips over their teeth. It is also why you can seldom understand the words a soprano sings in an opera, because there is not enough harmonic definition for some consonants and the sound of the vowels is altered by the tongue to give better projection!

Finally, the elasticity of the vocal ligament decides how high a female can sing. Some people have less collagen in their ligaments than others and so are more supple. Watch a gymnast. They can put their limbs into positions that other people can't. So can dancers. In fact, the lax ligaments that give dancers the ability to excel in their art is the reason that they are more prone to injury than any other type of performer.

Flexibility comes from having lax ligaments around joints, thus enabling them to have a greater range of movement. Such ligaments are thinner because they contain less collagen, and it is this lack that creates flexibility. To some extent this is genetic, but if worked on from an early age some joints can be stretched more than others. The hyperextension that Thai dancers show with their hands and fingers is a skill shared by most young Thai females. Not only do they practise it from an early age, but they also have genetically less collagen in their ligaments. Watch an 80-year-old grandfather in Bangkok squat under the back of a truck to avoid the rain – a thing no British octogenarian could ever do!

To sing above top F or G needs vocal gymnastics. It needs a hyperextendable vocal ligament. And you're born with that, in the same way as a dancer is born with ligaments that allow them to do the splits or kick high above the head.

Sopranos

There are basically four types of soprano voice. The *Coloratura soprano* is the highest female voice and usually has difficulty being heard in the chest voice range. They can usually be expected to range from middle C to F or G above high C. A typical role for such a voice is the Queen of the Night in Mozart's *The Magic*

Flute. Another role is in the more lyrical title role in *Lakme* by Delibes.

The Lyric soprano has a full, warm sound with a solid middle and has a characteristic beauty in the upper middle range. They would be expected to go from slightly below middle C to a high C. Mimi in *La Bohème* is a full lyric role and Susanna in Mozart's *The Marriage of Figaro* is a light lyric role.

Italian opera demanded drama and character in which Maria Callas excelled. The particular voice is called a *spinto* or *'pressed' soprano*. It is usually a much 'thicker' voice than the lyric soprano with a bit more edge and volume. Although it would be vigorously denied, a number of today's spinto sopranos use the musical theatre technique of 'belting' to add edge to the voice. While these sopranos specialise in the heavier works of Puccini or Verdi, they may move on to Wagnerian roles as they get older.

The final soprano is *the dramatic* soprano who will these days unashamedly 'belt' for certain notes. They are the loudest and lowest of the sopranos, usually with tremendous 'cutting' power. They will have a range from below middle C to a 'very pushed' high C. They are also suitable for Wagnerian roles such as Brunhilde.

Lower female voices

Mezzo Sopranos are, literally, medium sopranos. They have a darker quality than the dramatic soprano with a range about a third lower than the lyric soprano. They range from A or G below middle C to the A or B flat below top C. The two most famous mezzo roles are Azucena in Verdi's *Il Trovatore* and *Carmen* in the title role of Bizet's opera. Some operatic roles are written for women pretending to be men, and are known as the 'pants roles'. Cherubino in *The Marriage of Figaro* is typical of this sort of role as is Orlando in *Die Fledermus*. These roles are always written for mezzos.

There are few operatic roles written for *contraltos*, whose range is from G below middle C to G or A below high C. Ulrica in Verdi's *Ballo in Maschero* is one example, but most contraltos work in oratorio. There are those of 'a certain age' who will never forget the sound of Dame Clara Butt singing 'Land of Hope and Glory' at the Last Night of the Proms year after year! The vocal folds of a contralto are closer to the male in terms of bulk and size. Contraltos will all have a long neck so that the lower harmonics can find resonances. They will spend most of their time in the passagio or chest voice.

Tenors

People who never knew what a tenor was found out when Luciano Pavarotti sang 'Nessum dorma' as the theme for the 1990 football World Cup and then the Three Tenors, Pavarotti, Placido Domingo and Jose Carreras, made their famous record. Because a good tenor voice is much rarer than a good baritone voice their earning potential is the highest. They are the box office draw and get the best parts and the best money.

Thus insults about tenors litter the operatic world. A familiar saying is 'that there are men, there are women, and then there are tenors'. Hans von Bulow said that 'A tenor is a disease'.

Tenors are variously described as *Tenore di Grazie, Lyric, Spinto* and *Helden*. Many tenors will perform almost exclusively within one of these groups but as previously mentioned Placido Domingo started as a baritone and moved to tenor. At an early age he attempted to sing *Lohengrin* but judged himself unsuccessful. In his fifties he returned to Wagner to sing a perfect Walter in *Die Meistersinger* and then went on to record *Lohengrin* with great success.

A *Tenore di grazie*, which means graceful tenor, is a vocal athlete with a highly placed voice similar in mobility to that of the coloratura soprano. Such singers have a tremendous unity of tone over their entire pitch range. Outstanding examples of this type of voice are Ian Bostridge and Bruce Ford, who records extensively with Opera Rara. Both give a light seamless and tonally smooth performance especially in works by Handel, Rossini, Bellini and Donizetti. The voice has a one-register quality which is probably due to the seamless engagement of the head voice. The roles of Don Ottavia, Nemorino and Lensky could be seen as requiring grace and tonal continuity with early entry into the passagio and complete absence of strain or attack. These tenors must have an impeccable sense of rhythm and be very accurate in pitch. They do not require a climactic top note but must be able to sing their high notes with absolute ease. Since composers such as Rossini, who wrote frequently for

36

this type of tenor, ask them to sing a lot of top notes, their technique has to be solid and flawless. Almost all the Mozart repertoire for tenors requires a light singing mechanism which appears to cover the entire pitch range. The *tenore di grazie* will be expected to sing his roles with no apparent effort and without any noticeable negotiation of voice breaks.

The *Lyric* and *Spinto tenor* voices are what Verdi wrote for. Tenors with these qualities will have a lifetime's work in the Verdi repertoire. Lyrical singing is the voice type required for such arias as 'Celeste Aida', but the singer must also be able to provide the heavy climaxes of something like Cavaradossi's 'Vittoria' in *Tosca*. This voice should be capable of high pressure delivery and basically it has to sound just as 'macho' at high pitches. Its best known exponents today are Pavarotti, Domingo, and Roberto Alagna. These singers are also capable of light singing, but their habitual roles are not naturally light in performance. Ramades, Cavaradossi, Manrico and Otello are typical lyric spinto roles. They all require the delivery of climactic high Cs or B flats.

Some famous tenors who are more natural baritones find it difficult to reach high Cs in performance and they may have the music transposed down a tone when singing live. When they record however their high Cs can be inserted later from a single sung note – at the stroke of a finger on a keyboard.

The *helden tenor* is the Wagnerian tenor. He is often a baritone who finds that he can reach a high B flat. The helden tenor usually cannot attain the high Cs and Ds with ease but has a very strong lower and middle pitch range. They are usually physically large individuals who are strong men. I occasionally play golf with a helden tenor and I'm usually outdriven by a long way. Perhaps the most testing role is that of Seigfried; there are few roles that ask more of a tenor.

Singers who want to do the Wagner repertoire take a long time to develop, rather like front and second row forwards in rugby. Going too quickly into the Wagnerian repertoire is probably a mistake because the muscle power and the muscle stamina are usually not there. Generally speaking whilst Wagnerian singers have to sustain huge climaxes, they also have to be able to sing quietly far more expertly than in most other operatic roles. The huge dynamic range demands outstanding breathing technique and tremendous control over the tone of the laryngeal muscles in order to sustain low vibrato and high power capacity. It is the long legato phrases and controlled 'messa di voce' which mark a successful Wagnerian singer. The skill is to maintain optimum adduction of the vocal folds for mucosal drive and then to vary intensity simply by controlling the breath flow. This requires great physical strength and control in the laryngeal musculature. Singers have to create a tight and stable muscle platform with the vocal cords, so that even when singing with a low airflow, they can make the mucosa vibrate at a speed that produces a lot of harmonics. It is only by doing this and maintaining it, that there will be projection to an audience in soft as well as loud passages. No wonder some Seigfrieds get tired!

Lower male voices

The lower male voices are the baritone, the bass and the basso profundo. There is not a huge difference between the baritone and the bass. The high baritone will be asked to reach a G above middle C – but if he can do another couple of notes with good quality, he can get into the higher earning tenor repertoire. The bass will sing an E or an F above middle C but what he does better is to sing a good bottom E (and with a bit of effort a bottom C), whereas a baritone will only be good for a low G sharp. The so-called, bass-baritone bridges that divide.

As we have seen, muscle is the definer of frequency with males sounding lower than females because of their added mass of muscle at puberty. They also have more hyaluronic acid than females. This is one of the most hygroscopic substances known to man and with the fluid that it absorbs and retains, it adds a considerable mass to the cords. Heavier cords make a lower sound and it is the quantity of muscle and hyaluronic acid that decides if a singer is a bass or a tenor. The difference is only one of a few notes but it is the quality of these notes that is the important difference. With relatively little hyaluronic acid, the tenor will sing his lower register with a very relaxed thyro arytenoid muscle using every bit of weight he can recruit. Conversly, when he reaches the top of the register he only has to shift the weight of the thyro arytenoid muscle to let the vocalis take over in the lightened lengthened cords.

The bass singer on the other hand has no difficulty with the lower register because not only does he maximise the amount of thyro arytenoid muscle he uses but he also has the content of hyaluronic acid to add to the vibrating mass. His lower notes have a better quality than those of a tenor who has to maximise less mass. Similarly, at the top of the register, the bass will quickly become uncomfortable because he cannot 'shift' his hyaluronic acid as a tenor can 'shift' his vibrating muscle mass and so his top notes will quickly become thin and strained.

The basso profundo is almost a freak voice and can reach three to four notes lower than the normal bass. He may well be able to sing a good B flat which is 17 notes below middle C. This is the darkest and lowest of voices and is almost completely confined to the Orthodox Church and opera. The reason that so many basso profundos are from Russia and neighbouring countries is probably genetic. Just as different races have different facial characteristics so is it probable for them to have different internal structural characteristics. It would be reasonable to presume that Russian basso profundos genetically have more hyaluronic acid than their American or European counterparts.

The difference between the lower voices is not as marked as with the tenors. Baritones are loosely split into *lyric* and *dramatic*. There are very few roles in opera for the *lyric* baritone and he is probably more suited to music theatre because of this. The best roles are Papageno in *The Magic Flute* and Guigliemo in *Cosi fan Tutti*. Although Marcello is on stage almost throughout *La Bohème*, his is the least memorable role. The lyric baritone can usually manage the role of Pere Germont in *La Traviata*, but very few of the other Verdi roles.

The dramatic baritone is the pivotal voice of many of the Verdi operas – Rigoletto, Amonasro, Iago and the despicable Scarpia in *Tosca*.

The role of Escamillo in *Carmen* is a difficult one for either type of baritone to manage. Much of the bullfighter's music lies too low for a high baritone to project it successfully and yet it has high notes that are difficult for a bass baritone voice. The helden baritone is the big boned, big muscled, often dark voiced singer who specialises in Wagner – Wotan in the first three operas of *The Ring*, Telramund in *Lohengrin*, and Kurvenal in *Tristan*. The basso profundo does the Commendatore in *Don Giovanni*, the Inquisitor in *Don Carlos* and Sarastro in *The Magic Flute*.

Just as there are sportsmen like Michael Schumacher, Tiger Woods and Valentino Rossi who are *primus inter pares*, so there are singers who are just that little bit better than 'the rest'. We all have our views on who they might be so I'll refrain from mentioning names – we all realise that there is a factor X that enthralls us. So what is their secret, what do they do that others don't and why are they 'the best'? Because they have an inherent musicality and are able to control the fine muscles of the vocal cords so that the correct sounds pass to the resonating chambers.

The musical brain

If you're right-handed, then the left side of your brain makes your muscles work and it's also where your ability to speak and understand comes from. The right side of the brain, creates artistry and musicality. You make your larynx work by using the left side of the brain, but the expressive quality of your singing comes from the right side. There are, today, singers who have exquisitely beautiful voices, but you are not moved by the magic of interpretation of the song they are singing – only by the beautiful voice. That is a triumph of the left over the right side of the brain.

There are few things more painful than listening to someone singing or playing out of tune. Pianists have no problem in this regard because their instrument is tuned, string players position their fingers on the frets and to some extent can see what they do, and wind and brass players control the pitch with their lip muscles as well as the keys.

It's hardest for a singer, because to hit a note exactly they must adjust unseen laryngeal muscles to exactly the right length and tension. A poor singer may be just slightly off pitch, will hear the error, and will make the adjustment necessary. The listener will then hear them 'slide' onto the note. If a singer sings a long note, they must keep the muscles at exactly that tension for however long the music dictates. Moving between notes and keeping in tune is harder for a singer than it is for an instrumentalist because it is all about adjusting muscle tension – seamlessly.

Muscle control of the vocal cords

Singing is about muscle control. This is of course what separates the amateur from the professional, and the superstar from the merely good. It's what a singer does with the vocal cord muscles that determines what sound goes into the mouth and throat for 'further processing'. It is the fine control of the vocal cords that allow singers to produce bigger amplitude harmonics that can be further refined by fine adjustments of the muscles of the resonating cavities so that the voice is 'beamed' at 2–3 kHz.

The mucosal wave

Let's remind ourselves of what happens when you try to sing a note. You place your vocal cords together and blow air up from the lungs. As the air flows through the little gap between the cords, it sucks the mucosa off the underlying muscle so that a mucosal wave occurs up the edge of the cords. As this wave snaps apart, so we get a sound, provided the surfaces are wet. A male does this at about 100 times a second so the sounds merge and we hear a sung note at 100 cycles per second.

On page 18 there was an explanation of a laryngogram which displays the movement of every vibration of the vocal cord. You will recall that the vertical line represents the mucosal closure from below up and that at the peak of the curve, the mucosa is closed all the way up the edges of the vocal cord. As it separates, slower than it closes because the air flow is not sucking it inwards, the line of the tracing goes down and at the bottom the mucosa is back on the surface of the muscle. The next puff of air comes through and the cycle repeats.

The laryngogram is perhaps the best investigation to show the difference between a good and a 'not so good' singer. The 'good' singer will close the cords more quickly on each vibration and will have less space between the vibrations showing that each vibration is powered with a greater pressure. The significance of these two findings is that the signal will have larger harmonics and less air wastage. This means that the resonating cavities will have more to work with.

Harmonics

The sound produced in the larynx passes into the pharynx and mouth which are the resonating chambers. The larynx is not a harpsichord and therefore has resonance. This means that the sound is 'fuller', because it consists not only of the frequency that you produced but also large amplitude harmonics. As we shall see, the larger the harmonics you produce the better the chance you will have of your voice projecting. The quicker your mucosa closes in each cycle, the larger the harmonics produced will be. In other words, the more vertical the laryngogram upstroke, the better.

To understand how that produces bigger harmonics let's look at an analogy. Clap your hands and you hear the sound of a hand-clap. Bring your hands together slowly. They meet and if you listened carefully you might have heard a sound but possibly not. Bring them together as hard as you can. Big noise. So, the faster the closure, the bigger the sound: this is because a bigger acoustic signal contains bigger harmonics.

It's easy to demonstrate this with the hands, but what about the vocal cords? You can't lift them up and bang them together. Their faster closure could happen in either of two ways. Either the mucosa can move faster or it can move at the same speed over a smaller distance. If it moves faster then the frequency of the sung note rises, so this would be of little value. What it must do therefore is to move over a shorter distance. This is quite simply accomplished by setting the muscle of the cords marginally closer.

The vocal cord muscles set the vocal cords in the midline so that they can act as a stable platform for the mucosal wave to function. Their function is not only to vibrate but to allow the mucosa to vibrate, produce a sound and produce lots of harmonics for resonance. The muscle mass itself forms the platform on which the mucosal wave can function.

Muscle tone and stroboscopy

The muscle tone on each side must be exactly the same. One of the things that I always do when examining a singer is to look at the cords with a stroboscopic light. This lets me see the mucosal wave that is going along at hundreds of times a second, in slow motion. A stroboscope, which is an integral part of the video camera I use, is a light that flashes just out of synch with the frequency of the sound that is emitted. If the singer sings middle C (256 cycles per second) then the stroboscope flashes just below that speed. This allows me to snatch views of different parts of the mucosal wave cycle, integrate them, and show the singer the result in slow motion. This is recorded on video so that I can go over it frame by frame if required along with the singer.

This lets us see a number of things. The first and most obvious is to see if there is a mucosal wave or not. Singers in big trouble or who have had poor surgery on the cords may well not have a wave on one or both sides and they will not therefore have a singing voice. Indeed, they will probably have a hoarse speaking voice.

The second is whether or not the wave is the correct shape and whether or not it is symmetrical on each side. Altered muscle tension between the cords will produce an irregular wave and a poor voice.

I can study the wave over the whole singing range. I frequently see singers who have voice trouble only in a certain part of their range which may be the top, the bottom or the 'break' area. This could be due to a tiny lesion on the mucosa getting into a critical point and 'spoiling' the wave over one or two notes.

Earlier in this chapter I said that I couldn't tell the difference between Pavarotti's cords and David Beckham's. If however I saw a stroboscopic video, then the difference would be quite clear! I hope I do not do David Beckham an injustice, but Pavarotti's cords would be more stable and the mucosal wave would be bigger and more regular over a much bigger range.

If a regular, fast mucosal wave is to occur then the muscle and ligament of the cord has to form a stable base. There is no possibility of human muscle vibrating at even 20 times a second, never mind five or ten times that speed, and this is why the mucosa and not the muscle must vibrate. Furthermore, see how long you can contract a muscle and hold it in contraction. It won't be very long until the muscle at first hurts and then 'gives out'. To stop this happening in the larynx, the cords only use a bit of muscle at a time, rather like a 'Mexican wave' (see page 21).

Resonance

The operatic voice has to project over an orchestra that may number over 100, into a theatre where up to 3,000 people are sitting wearing clothes that are sound-absorbent. They are able to do that because of resonance. In the preceding chapter I pointed out that resonance involves using the 3 resonating chambers efficiently so that the harmonics are gathered at around the 3 kHz level and we can hear sounds easily.

But there's another aspect to resonance: it makes singing easier. I'll try to explain why this is so by another analogy.

Imagine a golf ball teed up on a frozen lake and attached to the tee by a stout elastic string. Hit the ball with a club and it flies off into the air and then along the ice. It will eventually slow as the elastic stretches and at a certain point it will become stationary. Almost immediately it will move again and return to the tee. It will race past the tee and travel the same distance backwards until it again has a momentary stop. The energy imparted to the ball to get it going is called kinetic energy. When the ball is stationary all the energy resides in the elastic and is called potential energy. This is perfect resonance and if there was no friction there would be perpetual motion. If you stood at one end of the ball's trajectory with a table-tennis bat and gave the ball a little hit every time it got to the extreme of its travel and was stationary, then it would travel even further and faster on the next journey.

So it is with the voice. Once resonance is established the singer can sing with much less effort because small amounts of energy from the larynx augment the resonance that is established in the vocal tract. It takes the weight off the larynx and the singer feels that 'the voice is riding on the cords' – which in fact it is! If a singer could not accomplish this there would never be an unamplified opera staged.

Harmonics are essential for good resonance. From colour plates 5 and 6 you can see the difference that fast vocal cord closure makes on the production of harmonics. The trained voice produces harmonics of much greater amplitudes than the untrained voice and this makes it much easier for the resonating cavities to recruit and gather them so that the grouping at 3 kHz makes the voice project and be heard easily without the aid of a microphone. And this is why an opera singer can make their voice carry over a large orchestra so that everyone in the theatre can hear them.

The vocal tract is measured from the vocal cords to the lips. In the average western male it is 17 cm and in the female 15 cm.

It consists of three chambers. The first is the tube through which the sound comes from the vocal cords to the pharynx (the supraglottis). The second is in the area of the tongue base and pharynx, and because of the flexibility of these structures the shapes of this area can be altered enormously. The third area is the oral cavity including the lips and palate. Each of these parts consists of cavities whose shape can be altered by the muscles in the walls. The length of the vocal tract can be altered by raising or lowering the larynx in the neck by means of the neck muscles that are situated outside the larynx, or by moving the lips forward in a round shape, or by pulling them back over the teeth. The harmonics produced from fast mucosal closure enter this tract. In order to get perfect resonance, a sound wave should be a quarter of the length of the resonating chamber. The male vocal tract will therefore have perfect resonance with a sound with a wavelength of 68 (4 × 17) and the female with a wavelength of 60 (4 × 15). What a singer does therefore is to change the length and shape of the vocal tract to match the wavelength of the particular note.

You will remember that fast mucosal closure produces bigger harmonics. As they enter the vocal tract they are collected together as bundles.

An analogy might be a dozen garden canes in a row – thin 'bendy' sticks. You grasp them in your hands and you have a bundle: if you struck something with it, it would have more power than using only one or even the dozen one after the other. These 'bundles' are called 'singers formants'.

The so-called 'first formant' is created in the whole tract and anyone can do this; it is in fact why even the worst of us can make some sort of attempt at singing. However it is not a powerful enough 'bundle' to project the voice. It's the sort of noise that would be heard perhaps in a pub sing-song, but in a theatre it would not be heard over an orchestra even in the front row.

The 'second formant' is created at the tongue base in the second resonating chamber. It is the one used by most tenors and gives a warm sound to a well-projected voice. It is the most important 'bundle' that a singer can create and may be used alone or together with the 'third formant'.

This is the one that adds brightness to the voice It is produced mainly by altering the shape of the third resonating chamber, the oral cavity. It is absolutely essential for sopranos and baritones. Sopranos, because this is their only chance to produce a 3 kHz resonance, and baritones because it lets their voice power match that of the tenor.

The best way to show what happens to the harmonics and indeed to show the harmonics themselves is via what is called a spectrogram. I always use this in the examination of singers because it lets me see what harmonics are being produced and what the singer does with them to enhance qualities such as warmth and projection. Colour plates 7–10 show a number of spectograms illustrating what can be learned from them. It is the recruitment of harmonics at the 3 kHz range that allows the voice to project and gives the characteristic 'brightness' that we identify with the classically trained voice. Not infrequently will I see singers who have a totally clear voice but the complaint is that the brightness or 'ring' has disappeared. Their spectrogram will not show the line at 3 kHz and with appropriate coaching, or more usually confidence building, they will re-learn to shape the resonating cavities to gather the harmonics or else get their vocal cords closer together so that the closure will be faster.

From these spectrograms we can also see how a singer produces their voice. For example, two of the greatest singers of a generation, Domingo and Pavarotti, sing the same notes to the same pitch but produce their voices in a completely different manner. Domingo, originally a baritone, has more harmonics to gather and this is seen on their spectrograms (colour plates 7 and 8).

Why sopranos are bad for your crystal

I'm sure that everyone has seen film clips of a soprano belting out a note near a crystal glass and shattering it. It's not a staged event – it can really happen and it has to do with resonance.

Every object has a resonance but you can demonstrate it in very few. One object where you can show it is crystal glass. Wet your finger and run it round the rim, or 'ping' the glass with your finger. It will produce a sound. Let's say for example that it is 600 cps. The glass now has to be placed on a firm surface and fixed so that it cannot vibrate. A soprano stands about five feet away and sings the same note. This sets up a resonance in the glass. Initially some of the sound escapes through the base and from the surface of the glass to the air, but a time will come when more energy is absorbed than is lost by the glass. The chemical 'springs' holding the glass molecules together break, and the glass shatters. In scientific terms the sound coming to, and being lost by, the surface of the glass is kinetic energy and that being absorbed by the resonance is potential energy.

The passagio

The management of the 'passagio' is one of the main factors that separates singers from non-singers. The ease, security and position at which it is done separates the good from the average singer. So what is it?

Most men find it easy to sing a few notes in the lower part of their range. There's no tension in the throat and the sound is acceptable. This is generally called the 'chest voice'. It doesn't come from the chest and the lungs do not play any unusual role. It doesn't resonate in the chest and you don't even 'feel' it in the chest! No matter – tradition has it that it's the 'chest voice'.

Women find it easier to sing in the middle part of their range. A woman singing along to the radio uses a much higher frequency than a man. This is known as the 'head voice'. Again it has nothing to do with the head. It doesn't come from the head, it isn't modified by the head and the head is basically just where the sound comes out!

If a man wants to sing high notes he will either 'cop out' and sing the note an octave lower, or when he does sing, the note will sound totally different from the chest voice. Similarly for the woman who wants to sing in the low part of her range or the very top of the range. So here are another couple of concepts that we have to address.

The first is that men have a point in their voice where they have to pass from one type of voice to another and the quality of sound changes. Women have two points where they pass from a normal speaking sound to an altered sound – one at the lower and another at the higher registers. These breaks are called the 'passagio'.

47

The passagio covers about five semitones. As the singer goes through this area they have to gradually change the shape of the muscle in the vocal cord from a wedge to a shelf. Think of it as the change you would have to make if you changed slowly from pouting lips to a closed-lip smile. Try it. Were you a bit wobbly? Little muscle twitches felt here and there? Try again and this time have the image of a snooker player moving the cue so that he hits a ball solidly, slowly and smoothly. Still wobbly? I'm not surprised. It takes a singer years to perfect this movement. What they have to do with their vocal cords is just the same as you have just tried with your lips.

At the point where they enter a passagio, a singer's thyro arytenoid muscle is almost fully tensed. I say 'almost' because if it were totally stretched then the sound would be getting rather stressed and the voice might be damaged by minor muscle tears. So the situation is that something else has to happen to the muscle mass to lighten it, because as mass is decreased so the frequency rises and the singer is able to reach higher notes.

The first thing a singer will do is to start to lengthen the cord by tilting the cartilages or else by letting the thyroid cartilage slip forwards on the joint. As the thyro arytenoid is stretched the wedge starts to turn into the shelf in the same way as a thick rubber band would be if stretched. There can be no other movement of the thyro arytenoid muscle other than passive change in shape with stretching, or else the edges of the cord would come apart, resulting in loss of the mucosal wave, loss of harmonics and loss of air pressure. The cord muscle has to stay together to keep the platform on which 'it all happens'.

Singers have to gradually withdraw the thyro arytenoid out of the vibrating part of the cord and leave just enough muscle to cover the ligament. This is because they require a platform over which a mucosal wave can travel so that harmonics can continue being produced. They also need muscle there so that tensions between the cords can be controlled, equalised and altered in a coordinated way. If there was no muscle then the vocal ligament would merely be acting like a whistle. This is what pop singers do in their upper range. With little or no vocal training they do not have the facility to carry out this fine controlled muscle movement and so they just turn their larynx into a 'whistle' and sing falsetto. Saying that, however, must be qualified by the fact that very little of the operatic

48

repertoire requires male singers to reach the heights produced by pop singers.

As the thyro arytenoid stretches, the last bit of muscle to be left opposing the other side is the specialised medial part of the muscle called the vocalis. To some extent this is capable of independent action and allows small, fast changes in vocal cord length, as demonstrated by a coloratura soprano doing fast runs.

It takes years to perfect this manoeuvre and the better it is mastered, the more chance a singer has of becoming a star. Poor technique here can to some extent be masked by muscle power, nearly always in males. Muscle power starts to diminish when the singer is in his forties and many careers become unhinged at this time.

Some older Italian teachers used to teach the passagio a semitone at a time – and a 'time' might be half a year, making the whole process take nearly three years! As the voice travels through the passagio many Italian teachers also describe it 'turning' – *girando*. It then turns into the head voice. For the tenor, this is where the excitement lies. There is nothing quite like hearing a tenor fill a theatre with his upper registers. Male lead singers in music theatre also frequently 'push' the chest voice to a level well beyond the area usually recommended for a passagio, but it is this almost scream-like quality that adds colour and meaning to the song. A soprano by contrast spends most of her singing career using the 'first' head voice, and it is only when she gets above her top A and approaches the top Cs Ds and Es that her second passagio occurs and further thrills the audience. Neither a mezzo nor a contralto do this second break.

The difficulty for baritones and also mezzos is to keep the quality of the head voice as similar to the chest voice as possible. For the higher baritones and mezzos who do not have so much muscle mass to keep out of the way it's easier than for a contralto or a bass, who often fight losing battles in the head voice.

What a singer has to do in the head voice is to keep producing the harmonics with the mucosal wave cutting the air flow as fast and as effectively as possible. Since they are higher in the register they don't need to be as large as in the lower ranges to focus them on the 2.5–3 kHz band. The closer they focus with their resonating cavities the more spectacular the 'ring' and the projection.

Vibrato

Vibrato is an effect that tradition expects from classical music. String players do it by shimmering their hand, as do brass and woodwind players. If singers want to do it they can't shake their heads or necks, but an operatic voice cannot exist without a perfect and regular vibrato.

There are many theories as to the source of vibrato in the operatic voice but the most persuasive to a medical doctor is the one that involves motor units. You will recall that muscle is made up of a series of motor units which consist of a few muscle fibres plus a supplying nerve. Big muscles like the thighs and the back that have to do only 'power' movements have only a few motor units because the muscles always work as a whole and only for a short time. In fine muscles like the fingers, the eyes and the vocal cords, the movements are precise and accurate and so greater neural control is required. To stop a fine muscle tiring, the motor units are used only a few at a time. They are used, then rested, then used again. The change occurs five times a second and it is this change that gives the characteristic 5 cps 'regular irregularity' to the classical singing voice.

It is not heard in the voice of a singer who is using amplification. If you use amplification then there is no need to produce big harmonics so that they can be gathered and projected at 3 kHz. This can be done a lot easier by the mixing desk! If you sing unamplified you will not be heard above an orchestra unless you gather at 3 kHz. That needs the stable platform with the cord muscle tensed so that the mucosal wave can function well.

The primary reason for motor unit recruitment is to stop the cords from tiring – and if a singer has to do 5 hours of Wagner in an evening that is important. The effect of this is the production of vibrato.

Vibrato can be voluntary or involuntary. Voluntary vibrato is what you hear when a blues or jazz singer wants to emphasise a climactic note at the end of a song or phrase. Theatre singers will also use it from time to time. It's accomplished by putting a tremor into some of the muscles from the larynx to the tongue.

An operatic singer however will have involuntary vibrato, which means they can't sing in full flow without it. This is because their vocal cord muscle tension has to be higher in order to keep the vocal cords just that little bit closer than normal so that harmonics can be created.

What vibrato is, therefore, is the regular 5 cps feedback mechanism of the human central nervous system, and it reflects the regular recycling of motor units in the vocal cords. It is an integral part of the classically trained voice and often spoils 'crossover' recordings made by famous divas. Cole Porter was not meant to be sung with vibrato and sounds odd when it is!

What vibrato *must be* is regular both in frequency and amplitude. A wide amplitude vibrato sounds like a yodel and an irregular frequency vibrato sounds like a drunk at the end of an evening!

5

The Music Theatre Voice

Music theatre as we know it today had its origins in the late nineteenth and early twentieth centuries. There have always been two types of opera. The one taking its roots from the initial works created for courts and courtiers, and the other being created for 'the people'.

The first type has never really lost its original 'baggage'. An evening at the opera not only draws opera lovers, but it is also where people go who want 'to see and be seen'. It is a place to go to show off jewellery, clothes and taste. Produce Wagner's *The Ring* in a theatre for 3,000 people and you will sell 3,000 tickets – but how many have gone because they are Wagner 'groupies' and how many are there to pretend that they know what it is all about, and who can *appear* interested for twenty rather tuneless hours.

The second type had its origins in the seventeenth century when John Gay wrote *The Beggar's Opera*. In Vienna in the eighteenth century there was a huge difference between the Vienna State Opera and the Volksopera. At the former you dressed up, and at the latter you went along in your day clothes and sat at tables with your friends, playing cards, talking and drinking while the singers and musicians entertained you. That was the environment for which Mozart was commissioned to write *The Magic Flute*. The next time you see it, think of it as a series of music-hall acts.

This form of opera became more stylised with the operettas written by composers such as Strauss and Lehrer, and it was clearly different from 'serious opera'. In music theatre, from the earliest times, the emphasis was on the words which told the story. They therefore had to be witty, amusingly rhymed and comprehensible within the frame of the music.

Would we have remembered Sullivan's music if it had not been for Gilbert's words?

The origin of modern music theatre

The first musical show that could be described as the forerunner of today's musical theatre was probably Jerome Kern's *Showboat*, which introduced the big Negro bass voice to audiences in songs such as 'Ol' Man River'. The soprano had lyrical songs such as 'Can't Help Lovin', that could be sung in the same style as in operetta with head voice and vibrato.

The inter-war years saw some operettas by the German composers Berthold Brecht and Kurt Weill, such as *The Threepenny Opera* which was the source of the song later recycled as 'Mac the Knife'.

In England, Ivor Novello and Noel Coward wrote many musical shows that were essentially plays set to song. The type of singing was suited to the upper-class English accent with its forward articulation in which sibilants predominated. The other essentially English characteristic that these works were meant to reflect was the essence of breeding and good manners – don't be showy or loud! Much of the lyric was therefore in an unvoiced form like speech, with long, held notes at the end of phrases. The quicker and clippier the words and the more multiple the rhymes, the better a song was judged to be.

At the same time, the new fashion for 'big bands' saw orchestras led by names such as Roy Fox, Geraldo, Henry Hall and Joe Loss. They usually played for dancing, especially in famous London hotels, and they had a lot of radio exposure. They had singers, who, by and large, followed the style of the London stage, with a wailing reedy sound that was above all 'neither loud nor showy'!

In America, a quite different sound was developing. The main songwriters were Irving Berlin, Cole Porter and George Gershwin. Many of their songs were in now long-forgotten stage musicals but they achieved popularity by wide radio exposure and occasionally via film musicals. The sound of the voice was above all *American.* The accent, the slang, the attitude of delivery and above all the 'pizzazz' made it totally different from the *English* sound.

The tunes were played by the major big bands who through the record industry and radio became widely known and the focus of attention. Bands such as those of Glenn Miller, Tommy Dorsey, Woody Herman and Harry James all had singers, some of whom, like Frank Sinatra, went on to have enormously successful solo careers.

The cinema started producing its own set of singing stars such as Al Jolson, Gene Kelly, Fred Astaire, Bing Crosby and Doris Day. The style of singing was quite different from the London stage and was based on the way that the big bands played jazz and swing. Who can forget the glamorous Busby Barkley musical productions which could never be matched on a live stage?

In the Forties and Fifties, Rodgers and Hammerstein wrote three memorable musical shows that were as successful in film as they had been on the stage. They were *Annie Get your Gun*, *Oklahoma!* and *South Pacific*. The baritone in these original productions and also in the films was Howard Keel, whose voice carried the 'manliness' of the American West, and the values of the 'American Dream' that pervaded the world at that time. It was almost an operatic voice, full of projection and vibrato. But it fitted.

Meanwhile, Sinatra, Martin, Como and Crosby were crooning their way into perpetual occupation of the hit charts.

Musical theatre voices

By now there were three elements of the modern theatre voice established: the American accent with the slurred Ts and Rs, the quasi-operatic voice and the crooner or lyrical baritone. A further three singing techniques used in stage musicals go under the names of 'twanging', 'belting' and 'falsetto'. The difference between these voices and the operatic voice, is that the latter does not need to use amplification.

The word 'belting' and the technique used to produce it are forever associated with the name of Ethel Merman and songs like 'Hello Dolly'. This might give the impression that it is a technique for the theatre and not for the opera house. This is false. While it would probably be strenuously denied, many modern operatic sopranos 'belt' at certain notes as do some tenors. So what is this rather odd-sounding vocal technique?

Basically it is a 'brassy' shout, but there is a very definite technique in producing the sound that differentiates it from a shout. In classical singing technique you keep the larynx low in the neck and don't put your head back. When you belt you have to lift the larynx in the neck and this is done by the two muscles that attach the thyroid cartilage to the hyoid bone, which is where the tongue is attached. As you put the head back, the cricoid tilts upwards, you tighten the neck muscles and push with the chest. You open the mouth wide, place the tongue flat in the mouth against the sides of the molar teeth and let fly!

This is the 'full monty', and is a method generally used in modern music theatre, but it's not quite what the operatic soprano or tenor does. They only use parts of it – the flat tongue, the wide mouth, the head back and the tightened neck muscles. It adds an 'edge' to their already natural 'ring' and is becoming more and more accepted – and more and more denied!

You might think that 'shouting' would be a way to shorten a singing career but it really is quite safe. People like Elaine Paige have been 'belting' all their lives and at an age when most singers are thinking of giving up, Elaine is singing better than she has ever done. The other thing that proves that it's a 'safe' way of singing is that London has at any one time about ten musicals running in the West End with casts of about 20 or more. So you have 200 singers belting six nights and two afternoons a week in the West End. If it wasn't a safe method of singing then the West End theatre would be littered with young, hoarse people – but it's not!

Twanging is the sound used in Country and Western singing. It is produced when the vocal cord signal is altered as it passes through the first resonating chamber, the supraglottis. This is the tube formed by the folds that connect the top of the arytenoid cartilages with the sides of the epiglottis. In classical singing you keep it as open and relaxed as possible so that as many harmonics as possible can arrive at the tongue base area, for modification before they pass into the final resonators of the pharynx and mouth. If, however, you tilt the epiglottis back a little and pull the apices of the arytenoids up, as you would do in swallowing, you constrict this tube and so the sound takes on a totally different quality. If you then pull the soft palate up towards the back of the nose and further narrow the gap by constricting the upper muscles of the pharynx, you'll begin to sound like an American. You'll have a nasal sound – add the accent and the language and you're all the way. Again this is a very safe voice because you are doing all the changes above the vocal cords which will come to no harm.

This is probably the most used voice and it sometimes produces problems for singers who have a long run in shows such as *Les Misérables*, where it is used most of the time. It has, in fact, become known as the 'Les Mis' voice, and before they audition for further parts in other shows, singers usually have to get some coaching to relax the pharyngeal muscles and stop the 'twang'.

The final voice type is the falsetto. There are three ways of producing this.

If you can move your cartilages apart sufficiently you will stretch the vocal cords to an extent that there is no functioning muscle, only a stretched ligament. In this case the cords act just like a whistle, and by making minor adjustments to the length and by moving the cartilages, the singer can change the pitch. There will be no vibrato and it is a suitable sound for the top of a harmonised song with other singers. It also adds interest to a solo-voiced song if used sparingly.

The second way is how coloratura sopranos do it. They stretch their lax vocal ligament but are able to keep the vocalis muscle in action. Even though they are singing very high this will allow a tiny mucosal wave to produce harmonics and a much more brilliant high note is achieved, possibly with some vibrato, depending on how much vocalis muscle they manage to integrate into the movement.

The final way is used by some counter tenors. They reduce the mass of the muscle by letting only the front part of their vocal cords meet and vibrate. This reduces the effective weight of muscle and allows them to sing high while maintaining harmonic production and also vibrato.

Again if used in pop and theatre, falsetto is a 'safe' way of singing, but it does need some innate muscle control and laxity of the vocal cord ligament, a gift that is not given to everyone.

Non-voiced singers

Since one of the greatest of the musicals, *My Fair Lady*, has one of the principles *talking* rather than *singing*, no chapter on musical theatre would be complete without describing the technique of non-voiced singing.

57

Some of the singers who have given the greatest pleasure have had almost no voice at all. Some never had any voice and others just grew out of whatever voice they had when they were young.

Rex Harrison made what was supposed to be a singing role, Professor Higgins in *My Fair Lady*, memorable by not singing! He was cast for the part because of his speaking voice and his appearance, but the story goes that it was only when filming began that they realised that his singing was embarrassingly bad! The director decided that the way out of the problem was merely to get Harrison to speak his lines and this not only worked but became the 'gold standard'.

Marlene Dietrich spoke rather than sang her two great hits, 'Lilly Marlene' and 'Where have all the Flowers Gone?'. She held the audience enthralled by her personality and presence.

Maurice Chevalier and Sophie Tucker performed until they were in their eighties, by which time any semblance of song had gone from their voices, but they still held audiences captivated with non-voiced singing. Who can forget Chevalier singing 'Gigi'. Nor should we forget the great French artiste Edith Piaff, whose idea of singing would be at variance with what most people understand, but who had a presence in her voice denied to most.

The introduction of the bossa nova to the American and European music scene was by the jazz tenor sax player Stan Getz. When he recorded 'The Girl from Ipenema' the singer was to be Brazil's top male singer, Joao Gilberto. In spite of numerous attempts, his English remained so awful that recording was impossible. The studio however had been booked and Getz wanted the record made. The problem was solved by his wife, who wasn't a singer or a musician at all. They got her to 'sing' it, because she had some idea of English pronunciation. Thus Astrid Gilberto, the mother of the present-day Inez Gilberto, made her name and fortune in the Sixties by almost speaking the words in a monotone.

The fastest-growing type of pop music in the last few years has been 'rap' which makes no attempt at song. The value lies in the beat, the words and the speaking voice.

Backing singers

The most usual place to see backing singers is behind pop groups. They're called 'vocalists' and move in time to the music, filling in with 'riffs' or 'wah wah' sounds when the soloist isn't singing. These are not freelancers but are usually an integral part of the group.

It is however an area that gives employment to lots of singers at the extremes of their careers: work that students, new graduates, past theatre singers and even past opera singers appreciate. Most are freelance and are on the 'books' of a person known as a vocal contractor or 'fixer'.

You probably never consciously listen to or even hear them. You certainly never *see* them. Think of films such as *Moulin Rouge*, *Harry Potter*, *Lord of the Rings*, *Return of the Jedi* and *Dinosaur.* You probably can't remember any singing, but there was lots. You might have thought that it was violins or synthesisers but it was singers. In fact, there were almost 60 backing singers employed for *Lord of the Rings*.

You'll remember lots of TV and radio adverts. You'll not only remember the visuals, the joke, but the words of the jingles. All done by backing singers who would be well paid. Backing singers will also do work on recording sessions acting as the 'choir' for famous soloists such as Russell Watson, and on TV spectaculars. The skill they need, and what keeps them on the 'fixer's' books, is an expertise in reading music accurately and quickly. They must also be experienced and adaptable, so that they can reproduce the sound that the conductor or orchestral director wants instantly, whether it be 'operatic' or 'flat'. Hiring recording studios is very expensive, as is paying lots of singers and musicians for a session. There can therefore be no hold-ups, explanations or practice time. It's all got to work first time.

Mixing vocal styles

The aim of music theatre and the classical Lieder form is the same. The singer is telling a story through text or verse and the audience should understand not only the sense of the song but the emotion that the composer wanted to transmit. In other words, the style of singing is driven by the text which, unlike grand opera, is as, or more, important than the music.

The big difference between Lieder and music theatre is that in the latter the singer is amplified. Projection by creating harmonics is not necessary and so all the words can be produced in a totally intelligible way. The difference that amplification makes is that the voice can be used in a more relaxed way and the mouth shape need not be altered when singing vowels to maintain the 'ring' of a classical singer.

Although a theatre singer can afford to colour the text they don't need to do it by altering their resonance and acoustic. That's what sound engineers are for! If a theatre singer in fact tried to produce the 3 kHz 'ring' vocally, then it would sound all wrong, as if a completely different sort of singer was performing. This is sometimes ill understood by opera singers using their operatic technique to sing, for example, 'The Cole Porter Songbook'. If the voice is lacking in brightness the sound engineers enhance the 3 kHz area and for even greater brightness should the song demand it they often add the 5 kHz resonance that boy trebles have.

Eva Cassidy has a beautiful voice and presents her songs with great artistry but apart from a moderately good 'belt' there is nothing exceptional in her technique. Her spectrogram (colour plate 11) shows that she has very little in the way of harmonics, but her sound engineers add brightness between 3 and 5 kHz.

When you speak, the thyroid cartilage is in the neutral position, and the vocal cords are short and thick to give a very direct quality of sound. Much of the repertoire for music theatre is in fact written to keep the voice in this area. While opera has to be high and loud, music theatre has other ways (electronic) of getting that effect.

So our singer is able to belt, twang, croon, do falsetto and do non voiced techniques. They will also have the ability to sing in the chest voice well above the area where a classical singer would go into the passagio, giving an exciting 'screaming' quality to the song. They know the words of the song and they have rehearsed with the sound engineers. They have a mike close to the mouth and the very best of electronic equipment to help them. All they need to do is to hold the pitch and sing in tune.

Thus, armed with these techniques the singer becomes a painter and uses the larynx and resonators as the mixing dish. They will mix style with resonance and with emotion. They will continually be constricting and relaxing the tubes of the larynx to change resonance and twang, increase and decrease the mass of the vocal cord for pitch, alter the plane of the larynx for falsetto, and alter the height and muscle control for brightness and belting.

This mixture has become the standard sound for the incredibly successful 30 years of the West End with shows such as *Les Misérables*, *Evita*, *Cats*, *Chess*, *Phantom of the Opera*, *Starlight Express*, *Sunset Boulevard*, and *Jesus Christ, Superstar*. Many of these shows have relatively similar melodies and harmonies but the great diversity of vocal performance allowed them all to sound very different.

6

The 'Popular' Voice

I had to think carefully about including a chapter on the voice used in 'popular' music in a book that was mainly about the singing technique used by the 'greats' of opera. The reason that I chose to write about it was that I, like the majority of other people in the world, like it enormously.

Seventy-five per cent of record sales are of singers of popular songs but this isn't surprising. Go to an opera and compare what you see with what you see at a pop concert. Which group of artists seem to be enjoying it more and which audience is having a better time?

This difference also manifests in cultural attitudes. Why is it considered 'better' to listen to a great baritone like Sir Thomas Allen singing, in a foreign language, about the miseries of a love-sick youth in late nineteenth-century Austria, than to listen to Billy Joel sing about the same issues in a language you can understand? Does Sir Thomas tell the story better? Is the musical accompaniment more interesting either harmonically or melodically? Probably not. Sir Thomas has a baritone voice that is controlled, well produced and effortless. He will move seamlessly from chest to head voice and back again. Billy Joel also has a light baritone voice that has a limited range and goes into falsetto when he has to increase the pitch beyond that which his laryngeal muscles can manage. Which is more beautiful or more enjoyable to listen to? It's like the difference between velvet and chocolate. You can't describe it. It's up to the individual.

Was it more meaningful to listen to the songs and music with which Benjamin Britten mourned the devastation of war in his War Requiem, than the harrowing voice of Joan Baez as she mourned the fact that so many young American lives were being lost in a pointless war in Vietnam?

The first performances of *Figaro* were banned. It was unthinkable that the concept of a servant outwitting a master could be given public airing. The revolution brought in by 1960s rock brought out similar prejudices. It has always been so. And it is due to this type of societal judgement that the two types of music have diverged.

Not everyone either wants to or has the ability to be an opera singer, but anyone who wants to can try to be a pop singer. The pop scene is one that fascinates millions of people, not all of whom are young, because for many it represents the most memorable and most vivid parts of their lives. In historical terms it is a measure of fashion, of society and political attitudes set to music. It has been populated by characters some of whom were outstanding musicians and some who were memorable 'images'. The admitted excesses of Sir Elton John and Sir Mick Jagger make stories about Billie Holiday and Charlie Parker seem inconsequential.

The voice in pop

In pop, the quality of the voice does not need to be what other genres would describe as 'good'. It is all about image. Alongside image there are the words. These express the image that the band or singer stands for and it is these factors that will develop their following and thus their success.

For recording purposes the engineers can make up for all but the worst type of voice or support it with some good professional backing singers. With a 'presence filter' they can add 15–20 decibels at the important 3 kHz frequency so that the singer, even though they're amplified, can be heard above the band. Since the music is recorded on to digital tape they can get pitch stability control, correct the 'slide' into a note when the singer has hit the wrong pitch and can silence noisy amplified breathing.

I am not wholly dismissive of the voice qualities required for pop singing, and it goes without saying that there has to be a certain quality for the sound engineers to work with. The basic skills that an aspiring pop singer must have are the ability to sing in tune, to be able to hold a legato note at the correct pitch and be able to breathe properly so that they never lose power or control of their air flow. Let's look at these basic voice skills one by one and relate them to what 'superior' singers might be doing.

In order to sing the note that is required, as opposed to another that might be a few hertz away from it, the brain needs to have a reasonable perception of pitch. Rather than the actual note being the important aim of a singer, it has to be that note in relation to the previous one. If this skill is lacking, then the potential star will either sing so badly out of tune that their career will have no future or they will 'slide' into the note. A singer who habitually does this might make it a feature of their performance but by and large, unless their image is fantastic, there will be others who only do it occasionally and who can be corrected by the sound engineer.

Holding a 'legato' note requires some of the skills of a classical singer. They have to hold the vocal cord muscles still, in order to form the stable platform for the mucosa to vibrate with no wobble. It needs a reasonable air flow and an ability to recruit motor units regularly so that the muscles do not tire.

Control of the air flow is as important for the pop singer as it is for the classical singer but for different reasons. Of course there has to be an air flow of a certain power to make the mucosa vibrate, but due to the use of amplification, it can be used to get a breathy effect that many songs, especially ballads, require.

Indeed there are some pop artists who can sing and who have had some training. For example, out of the three males who fought out the final of the first Pop Idol competition, two had been choristers as boys. Two of the best British female singers of today, Annie Lennox and Dido, had a classical training, while another, Sophie Ellis-Bextor takes regular singing lessons. Although few have gone along the path of classical training nearly all will keep in regular touch with a voice coach such as Paul Farrington or Mary Hammond. Among the female singers I think have naturally good voices I would list Mariah Carey, the late Eva Cassidy, Alicia Keys, Beverly Knight, Dido, Sophie Ellis-Bextor and Christina Aguilera. The 'best' male voices are Bono, Robbie Williams, Ronan Keating, Elton John, Rod Stewart, Phil Collins and Brian Adams. Justin Hawkins, singer with The Darkness, makes use of his wide range, hitting falsetto notes in a distinctive style.

Jazz singing

The origin of the blues and later jazz forms was gospel music which had its foundation in the Southern Baptist church. In a church choir singers would learn rhythm, vocal quality, stamina and the ability to build and hold a climax which is also the requirement for Wagnerian singing. Some gospel singers used a lot of artificial and wide amplitude vibrato, especially in the long holding notes, but it is a technique that is used sparingly, as opposed to classical singing where it is a constant feature and an integral part of the technique.

Black gospel music as opposed to Christian gospel (or white gospel music) is a black cultural form based on the lessons of redemption and freedom in this world and the next. Whereas the original words were of freedom from slavery, the concept of freedom from segregation took over. In this way black gospel music is contemporary, but the Baptist Church-based form still relates to the saving of the soul and the afterlife.

This type of singing is more related to opera than Lieder, even though the words carry an important message. Although it is word- rather than music-based, the words must be heard and understood and they have to carry 'punch'.

It is in fact one of the most vocally strenuous types of singing, even though in big arenas amplification is used.

Singers like Mahalia Jackson and Bessie Smith were the American equivalent of England's Clara Butt, in size, range and quality of the voice. The head voice was often in falsetto mode but it was usually well produced, with harmonics; vibrato was 'switched' on and off for effect rather than being ever-present and automatic.

The voice was in the mezzo and often the contralto range because these large ladies had long resonating passages and so were able to produce the lower range with excellent quality. Belting of course was the basis of the impact necessary to give the message its drive.

Traditional jazz started in New Orleans at the end of the nineteenth century. It was mainly an instrumentally based art form but some of the gospel singers brought their vocal technique to it. The songs of traditional jazz were word-centred as well as depending on the voice to act as the saxophone that wasn't there. Vocal excellence depended on the intelligent use of amplification, stamina, power, pitch holding and above all, presentation. Most songs were blues based and about sex, love, drugs and hardship. Nearly all the songs involve sex, using euphemisms such as 'melons' 'shakin trees' and 'buyin' love'. In fact, in their day, they were just as shocking as many of present-day rap's sexually explicit lyrics.

There are very few examples of good singing from traditional jazz. It was not really a music designed for voice apart from improvising like the saxophone. Short phrases would be sung to get impact and there is hardly a tune in the classic trad jazz repertoire that has a long song line. The vocal range needed was less than an octave, and most of the singers whose throats had been turned to skin by active and passive smoking, only had a limited range.

After the mid Forties and the experiences of thousands of black Americans in Europe, black consciousness was developing, and part of that was expressed in the new jazz style of bebop. Bands were still segregated and it was impossible for whites to play with blacks. Bebop began in New York in a club called Birdland, and when one of its main developers died, New York subway walls had grafitti declaring that 'Bird Lives'. Bird was the great Charlie Parker, who, along with the trumpeters Dizzy Gillespie and Miles Davis, and the pianists Bud Powell and Thelonious Monk, developed this fast and furious form of jazz.

The main change was the use of harmonic structure that had a particular sound to it, as opposed to the straightforward chords of traditional jazz. Thirteenths, elevenths, added fifths etc., gave the music a new base and on top of this flew the lightning fingers of the instrumentalists. At the speed they played there was little that a singer could do other than 'scat' which is merely making sounds at high speed to imitate a solo from a sax or a trumpet. The singer would do a wordless improvisation, with a 'doobee, doobee' type of lyric, using falsetto frequently to copy the two- or three- octave range of the trumpet or sax.

It's not surprising therefore that very few singers emerged from this period. The only one that did, Billie Holiday, did so for the wrong reasons. Her life, like that of Charlie Parker, was controlled by drug abuse and she, like Parker, died an early drug-related death.

Crooning

This was the use of a light baritone voice with good microphone technique, sympathetic musical accompaniment combined with an attractive appearance. Diction and phrasing were all important. Although it sounds easy to impersonate, there is a skill in keeping in tune and especially on the long legatos that are such a feature of the style. Control of air flow is vitally important, as is tight closure of the whole length of the glottis to avoid air escape which would of course be exacerbated by the close amplification.

Female crooners would use a mezzo-soprano voice in the chest register. Because of the anatomy of the female glottis with air escape almost inevitable at the posterior part, a breathy quality can be turned into an attractive feature.

The 'classical' popular singer

I rank Frank Sinatra and Ella Fitzgerald as 'classical' because of their vocal and artistic talent. Their spectrograms in full voice are shown in colour plates 9 and 10 and it should be obvious that the patterns are not dissimilar to those of Pavarotti and Callas. On spectrograms we can distinguish which harmonics are natural and which have been added by recording engineers. These singers were not taught to produce the voice 'operatically' but had they been, the result would have been an equally successful operatic career.

The diction of Sinatra and Fitzgerald is unequalled by any Lieder singer I have heard, and their phrasing adds an originality and uniqueness to their songs that will be long remembered. Similarly, their control of pitch, breathing and vibrato is faultless.

The main difference between classical and standards singing is the range used. Most female singers will use the range between the G or F below middle C to the C above middle C, and this they can accomplish in ordinary chest voice. This type of singing is much closer to the spoken voice than classical singing and a singer could quite easily turn a word into a note in the same voice.

Many popular singers take or have taken classical lessons but they have to have a teacher who is skilled in both genres. If a female singer wanted to sing top Gs then a classical teacher would show her how to produce the voice in the head style with the resonators and vibrato pattern of other classical singers. But this would sound totally alien in the popular idiom. This is why records of popular music featuring famous classical singers usually sound quite wrong.

Country and Western voice

Country and Western music, and its multiple sub types such as country gospel, country rock etc, had its origins in Nashville, Tennessee. The voice type is simple. It is almost entirely twanging and the articulation is Southern. Nashville is pronounced 'Niayash-ville'. This is the type of voice quality used by Dolly Parton, Johnny Cash and more recently, Shania Twain. It is so typical that when non American singing students are taught to twang they are told – 'Think Country and Western'.

7

The Earliest Pop Idols

It would be a pretty fruitless exercise to try to pinpoint the first moment in time when a person sang. I just don't think that there was ever a moment when someone said 'What did you just do with your voice there Ed?' Tale-tellers probably used some sort of song to pass down their oral traditions, but the main influence on singing as we know it today was undoubtedly the Church.

Church music, women and surgeons

For the first thousand years after Christ, the world was ruled by the Church. The Church ruled people not only in this life but also in the next, and since most people believed in a life hereafter that extended into infinity with the alternative to a believable heaven being an even more believable hell. So laypeople, did exactly what the clerics said they should do.

Pagan religions had employed chant and song during their worship and so while one cannot date it, song became an integral part of the original Christian rites. The earliest chants were Jewish and employed only one or two notes to a syllable. Although there would be some primitive melodic line, there would be no rhythm, and the lines were merely chanted by the worshippers to no particular tune.

More melody and polyphany came from Greek and Byzantine influences. Today almost every small sect claims that it is the fastest growing religion and while I do not wish to enter a quantitative or qualitative debate we cannot disclaim the fact that today the Pentocostalists have some claim in this respect. There obviously

71

must be more than 'happy clappy' to the religion, but certainly the happiness engendered by song must play some part in its popularity. So regardless of what the present-day fashions are, there is no argument that song has always been a great way not only to declare the faith but also to get converts. And then there was the sexy bit. By the third century AD it was common practice for men and women to alternate singing verses and to sing choruses together.

But this 'happy singing' was not allowed to continue. The Church decided that, on balance, worship was not meant to be enjoyable, and it also suspected that it brought out some of the baser instincts in man. And of course the preaching of ordinances such as obedience and self-denial were opposed to that. Celibacy was in and sex was out. Warm, mellifluous female voices were therefore thought to be bad for males and liable to take their minds off whatever it was they ought to be thinking of. By AD 318 the Church was so upset at what it thought women's voices might be doing to men, that it banned the sound of women's voices in church.

It got worse. By AD 367 men weren't allowed to sing either and only specially trained clergy were allowed to create song in church. Women singing was regarded as an admission of promiscuity! In the fifth century, Bishop Hippolytus declared the following edict: '*A woman who attracts people with the beautiful but deluding sweetness of her voice must give up her trade and wait forty days if she is to receive communion*'. He did not, however, define 'her trade'. A hundred years later, Bishop Augustine said: '*How many peasants and how many women know by heart and recite out loud the Devil's songs, erotic and obscene?*'

Since I am a descendant of the barber surgeons perhaps this little tale will be of interest. Abbeys had two sorts of cleric. The superior orders were professional churchmen who were destined to climb the slippery pole that might lead to the papacy or at the very least an archbishop's job. The lower orders, the brothers, tended the gardens, cleaned the houses, cooked the food and cut the hair. They were very much 'delta people' and did not have a clear career path to the top. The ones that were my forebears were the brothers that cut hair. Since they had the sharp instruments they also performed surgery, such as incising abscesses, bandaging fractures, bleeding and perhaps stitching lacerations. In 1215, Pope Innocent III decreed that the superior orders should no longer take part in execution, torture or surgery! That left the lower orders with a clearer job description. The brothers that cut hair then split into two groups. The meek and mild continued to cut hair and became the 'barber tonsurists' and the hooligan element became the 'barber surgeons'.

The first stars with long hair

By stopping laymen and women singing, the Church created the world's first pop idols. The priests who specialised in singing were called 'canons' at their ordination and were charged to *'see that thou believe in thy heart what thou singest with thy mouth, and approve in thy works what thou believest in thy heart'*. Their art grew. They were soon introducing ornaments to the melodic line and quickly became 'stars'. In his book on early singing, W. J. Henderson tells us that *'they speedily acquired the self glory which has clung to singers ever since ... and began to swell their vanity'*. They also predated the Beatles by growing their hair long, since it was believed that this added to the effect of their singing.

They trained at the Scuola Cantorum, which was founded by Pope Gregory in AD 590 and the course lasted nine years. During that time they would memorise all the chants and presumably learnt articulation and breath control in order to sing long legato lines. So it was rather curious that while the Church was actually trying to prevent people from singing, they were developing education systems that were studying and refining the art. Meanwhile, the only women allowed to sing religious chants were nuns – but they were taught to sing in a disembodied fashion that was 'sexless'.

It was of course impossible to prevent secular singing, and man would continue to express his views on life, and life subjects, in song. Singing also became associated with spells, magic and medicine. St Augustine once said that *'when we have a headache we flee to the singers of incantation'*. However, the Church still wanted to control the music business and denounced all secular songs, love songs, work songs and folk songs as 'sinful and lascivious'.

By the eleventh century, the Dark Ages were passing and people were beginning to express themselves as individuals. As part of this, secular singing increased, and it was then that the first solo singers of note came along; they were known as troubadours.

How singing bankrupted England

Their repertoire could not have pleased the Church, which had spent the previous thousand years suppressing women and sex, because the first songs involved lavish praise for women and their virtues. Most troubadours would be accomplished musicians and singers with the ability to project the voice.

The so called, *jongleur* was a one-man vaudeville show, a one-man band, a singer, a stand up comic and a magician. As time went on, the art form attracted people of noble birth and even royalty.

The most celebrated 'troubador' was probably Richard the Lionheart, who was a celebrated composer and singer of chivalric love songs. His co-songwriter was Blondel de Nesle, and it was he who supposedly found Richard when, returning from a crusade, he had been imprisoned and held to ransom in Hungary. Legend has it that Blondel found his way to the castle prison, crept up the rock till he was under the appropriate window, and sang a song that he and Richard had written. He heard Richard take up the song and thus he knew he'd found him. History suggests that he might have been better keeping 'shtumm' because the ransom that England had to pay just about cleaned out the Treasury!

From the music that survives today we know that the sort of songs that were sung required a range of not much more than an octave and that the common interval was the fifth. The emphasis was on the words rather than the quality of the voice and the quality of sound would have been not unlike that made by the crooners of the 1940s (apart from Sinatra!).

At the same time, the *minnesingers* developed in Germany. With typical Germanic thoroughness, they made up rules for singing that had to be rigidly followed. There were also rules that applied to the composition of songs, rules that Wagner made fun of in his opera, *Die Meistersinger von Nürnberg*.

By the end of the fifteenth century, a number of composers were writing music for various parts and this of course required a mixture of low and high voices. The major composers came from the Netherlands and the music required voices of power and stamina.

The Church had depended on boy trebles singing the higher parts in Church music until then, but their voices did not have the stamina or power necessary for the new music. To castrate a male and thus interfere with his sexuality and his ability to procreate was considered to be tampering with the will of God, and so the Church threatened excommunication to anyone participating in such a crime against nature. Pragmatic to the end however, the Church took the view that if a male with the voice of a female turned up on the doorstep so to speak, and was able to sing well, then it was just God's Will and the Church's good fortune! Of the castrati, more later.

The beginning of opera and pop

The earliest known play with music that was independent of religious subject matter and Church patronage was *Le Jeu de Robin et de Marion*, written around 1283 by a Frenchman, Adam de la Halle, and composed for his employer, Charles d'Anjou who was also King of Sicily.

In Italy in the fourteenth and fifteenth centuries, Latin and Greek plays such as the comedies of Plautus and Terence were frequently performed. Opera, in fact, came about by mistake. Greek plays are delivered in exclamatory style and they chose singers to play the parts. They sang rather than exclaimed and so we had the 'musical play'. Also, these plays started to have musical intermezzi which started merely as a way of signalling the end of each of the usual five acts, but gradually began to take over.

One of the main things that people wanted to see, however, were the special effects that accompanied these presentations. The stars therefore were neither the singers nor the composer but the 'machinests' who created the effects!

The third building block of opera was the play *Orfeo*, in which Orpheus charms the gods with his voice. The message was getting through! This was the background to opera as we know it today, with music used to express moods, pictures and stories in dramatic form.

The development of the modern operatic singing voice very much parallels the development of mankind. With the Renaissance and the age of humanism, men began to emerge as individuals. Until then man had been part of a feudal unit, and in singing had been part of a polyphonic structure. At a time when mankind was allowed to believe that an individual was unique and not just part of a whole, solo singing established a claim to that uniqueness.

The first operas were for courts not for the mass audience. Jacobo Peri probably wrote the first opera, *Euridice*. He himself was a singer and a member of the Camerata in 1600. The opera is modelled on Greek theatre and has a concentration on the word rather than the music. The style is traditional declamation.

This sort of composition was taken forward by Claudio Monteverdi, the son of an apothecary and barber surgeon. His opera, *L'Incoronazione di Poppea*, was first produced in 1640 but it had originally been a more minor church work produced in 1582. The most interesting thing about this work is that it was the first time that a paying public had been able to get access to opera as an art form.

The early critics and market-makers

Today it's easy to market a good idea. We have TV, film, radio, records and magazines. How do you collect and distil the information on a new art without these tools? Well that was addressed by a group of Florentine intellectuals and aristocrats who had a common interest in music and who formed themselves into a society called the *Camerata*. They met in the house of the Count of Vernio, Giovanni de Bardi, and one of them was Gallileo Galilei's father, Vincenzo Galilei. This was between 1573 and 1592 and the Renaissance was in full flow, led by the Medici family of Florence. New art from Michelangelo and Leonardo, new writing from Dante Alighieri and new music. Composers such as Monteverdi were moving from composing solely for church functions to creating a new art form. He and others were taking ancient Greek plays and basically presenting them as musicals performed by solo singers, choral singers and an orchestra.

The members of the Camerata became the equivalents of the football 'scouts' of today and searched for singers who could take leading roles. They would probably hear them first in churches, singing solo parts in requiems and masses. To a fixed format they then had to describe the singer's qualities so that the decision as to their suitability for a part could be assessed by their colleagues. They used such phrases as the 'beam' of the voice, alluding to the way in which the voice took the ability to be projected like a light beam. To this day, many teachers still perceive sound in this way.

In Italian it became known as the *colonna* or 'column' of the voice. The effect that they were trying to describe was, we will later see, the essential acoustic 'trick' that a professional singer must accomplish in order to sing unamplified to a huge audience.

The Camerata interviewed singers of the day and noted the ease with which these 'naturals', as they were called, covered a wide musical pitch span, and described the bright quality of their voices. They developed a methodology of interview so that they could begin to understand the technique of singing. As opera developed, the requirement for enhanced or 'trained' voices grew and success in opera offered good financial reward and status well above that of a musician.

The early work of the Camerata thus developed into teaching methods that captured the sort of voice that they deemed correct for the new art form of opera. They were looking for a bright voice quality and relaxed, easy voice production. The Camerata were therefore not only the first critics but the 'setters of style'. They would in fact have been the jury in *Pop Idol*!

8

Will Young Wasn't the First Manufactured Star

In the last few years we have watched our TVs and admired the skill of pop marketers who use TV to produce absolutely certain profits. Start with a few hundred hopefuls. Get the public to decide week on week who they like best. After all, these are the people who will buy the end product – the record, or records that the winners will make. It's an absolute 'cert': before you go to the expense of making a record in a studio, you create something that is bound to be successful.

The TV companies will make money from huge viewing audiences, the public will get great pleasure watching the triumphs and humiliations of the kids, and at the end they, the public, will virtually tell you what they will buy. A better way to make money out of music has never existed before.

But there is a precedent.

The need for the manufactured singer

Imagine this situation 400 years ago.

Polyphony, or the singing of music in parts, was the most popular form of music. All the 'big events' were run by the Church. A sung mass was not only worship but 'show business'. Everyone enjoyed it. You needed four types of voice to sing the various parts – basses, tenors, altos and sopranos. Generally speaking, the latter two were females. But the patrons of the music had decreed that they didn't want women singing because that was 'bad' for men. Something will always fill a void in the market, and in this instance it was a group of Spaniards who were able to sing the alto and

79

soprano parts in a falsetto tone. Fine, but it's a bit like getting a counter tenor like David Daniels to sing the Whitney Houston 'song book'. The little boys in the choir could provide the high soprano lines, but they sounded like little boys. Their voices were clear and high but lacked power. Trouble was that as little boys grew bigger and got more power, their voices became deeper, and you lost a good singer.

If only you could do something to let those little boys grow up and become more powerful but stop their voices getting lower. The Church must have known that castration was the answer but to condone this would be a sin against God's perception of human behaviour. There was no possibility that the Church could set up 'castration units' as recruitment reservoirs for choristers, even though the songs they sang were 'to the greater glory of God'. But pragmatic as always, the Church did not regard it as a sin against God if a young man happened to turn up for an audition with a choir with a voice not only like a soprano but with a power that had never before been heard from a female soprano.

Here then is the dreadful story of 200 years of the castration of goodness knows how many little boys – for the 'glory of song'!

The history of castration

Castration had been practised since earliest times for various reasons. Some pagan cults, like the Cybele, insisted that their priests were castrated. The Romans and the Greeks practised it because they needed African eunuchs to look after their homes. If it happened to an African he wouldn't be surprised because for centuries defeated enemy tribes had been castrated to stop them breeding. Muslims had also performed castration on harem keepers for very obvious reasons. There are also records of medical men performing castration for the cure or prevention of leprosy, madness, epilepsy, testicular cysts, gout and various inflammatory conditions.

To understand why castration was essentially an 'Italian thing' you have to understand Italian rural life. Every family in the Italian countryside used to keep at least one pig. A mother pig will usually produce around 12 piglets. There was a law decreeing that pigs, both male and female, should be castrated, because when they were eaten they tasted better. A castrator would travel the region doing the necessary. Immediately after Christmas the pig would be killed by the family and neighbours. They would hold down the animal, put a hook under its chin and cut its throat. The blood was kept for black pudding, the covering of which are the cleansed intestines. Once all the organs were removed, the pig was beheaded and split in two. The area of Italy which had the most pigs was Norcia in Umbria. And that was where the first castrati came from!

The first castrati

The first castrati were admitted to the papal choir in 1599 – and the last one sang in that choir in the Sistine Chapel on the eve of World War I in 1914.

It was probably no accident that the first two castrati in the papal choir were from Umbria: Pietro Paolo was from Foligno and Girolamo Rosini was from Perugia. Both of these places are close to Norcia. When the two Umbrians were admitted to the choir there was a revolt by the Spanish singers who had until then had control over the soprano and alto parts. It didn't last long, and it wasn't successful, because the quality of the castrati voice was something that people had never heard. It had the power and control of the male, and the fullness and beauty not of a soprano or an alto, but somewhere in between – and that was original.

The fact that the Italians were the greatest consumers of these singers was not only due to the fact that the Church had excluded women. They also *enjoyed* the new quality of this soprano voice in church choirs. Castrati were therefore given a degree of respect by the Italians.

In Italy, most Catholic families were large. More mouths to feed in poor families meant that there was not enough money to feed all. Agriculture in the south of Italy in the seventeenth century was rather like nineteenth-century work in the docks. A foreman would come to a village, ask for a certain number of men to work for a day doing a specific task and then perhaps not reappear for some weeks. The average southern Italian peasant was lucky if he got 100 days' work in a year if he did not own land. So another child was an economic disaster even though the priest was pleased. So parents who had huge families were willing to let their little boys be castrated because there would be one less mouth to feed and the little boy would be well looked after. There was also the possibility that they might make enough money to help the rest of the family.

In the early days it was probably the pig castrators who did the operation. Whoever did it had to be a quick surgeon because there were no anaesthetics. Also they were almost certainly skilled operators because if there had been any sort of serious mortality even the hardest-hearted, meanest parent would not have subjected their child to the operation.

Even though castration started in central Italy it became much commoner in the south of Italy, which curiously was not governed by the Vatican but by the Bourbons, as part of the Kingdom of the Two Sicilies. The papal states were present-day Rome, Lazio, Umbria and the Marches. There were few castrati from the northern states of Piedmont and Lombardy.

The boy selected for castration would have shown an aptitude for music and would have an outstanding treble voice. The catalyst would be a choirmaster who might be the local priest or a music-loving patron who would identify the child, arrange for the operation and arrange further education at a music conservatory. To the family this was probably wonderful. There would be plenty of other children to work, there would be one less mouth to feed, and there was the possibility of sharing in future riches if the boy became successful.

The castrati voice was attractive and there was a ready market for it not only in Church music but also in the new entertainment form – opera. In fact it is now virtually impossible to revive the music of Cavalli and Allesandro Scarlatti because it was written purely for this type of voice.

The surgery

The operation involves removal of the testes along with the spermatic cord and blood vessels from the scrotal sac. There are no records of the technique used and so we can only guess.

The type of castration performed in gender transformation today involves removal of the contents of the scrotal sac with preservation of the skin which is then turned inwards to the perineal floor to create the labia of the vagina, while the penile skin is infolded to form the actual neo-vagina.

Since no anaesthesia was available in the seventeenth century, whatever was done had to be done quickly. The first anaesthetic was not in fact discovered until 1846. Usual anaesthetic agents in those days were alcohol or opiates. There were no injection techniques available and drinking opiate concoctions would as likely as not have been followed by vomiting prior to sufficient absorption. In other recorded operations of the time the so-called 'soporific sponge' was used. This was literally a sponge soaked in morphine, hyoscine and lettuce extract!

It is likely therefore that both scrotal sacs were excised together with their contents using a very sharp instrument. You can bleed to death from a cut artery because the heart creates the pressure with each beat to force blood out of the cut vessel and the bleeding stops only when the heart does not have enough fluid left to pump around the body; and by that time you are almost dead. If a vein is cut the blood that comes out was on its way back to the heart and is not under so much pressure as blood being pumped directly into an artery. If you apply pressure to a cut vein, sooner or later a clot will form and the bleeding will stop. When arteries are cut quickly, however, they often go into spasm and the arterial wall muscle closes off the mouth of the vessel so that there is virtually no bleeding. It is unlikely that ligatures would have been applied to any cut vessel and so almost certainly the method was to cut off the testicles at their base with a very sharp knife, very quickly, and then to apply pressure to the cut surfaces until the venous bleeding stopped. Death from blood loss would be most likely to occur if the knife was blunt or if the cut was not completed with one movement.

The most likely cause of operative death would however be from infection. In the seventeenth century, death from illness or childbirth was part of life. The maternal mortality rate from bleeding or infection would have been about 1 in 50 or so. Surprise would not therefore be expressed if a little boy died after a castration. The death rates reported were anything between 10 and 80 per cent and the appropriate rate would depend on where it was done.

In the Maria Nova Hospital in Florence in 1715 there was a room with eight beds for boys who had been castrated, so it is likely that surgeons did mass castration 'lists' in the same way as tonsils were, until recently, done.

Castrations were also done in back streets and on farms. I doubt if the death from infection would be any worse in these environments than in hospitals because then, as now in the UK, hospitals were greater reservoirs of infection than houses.

Physical effects of castration

Although a child might reach puberty by the age of eight, it would be very rare and likely to be part of a genetic syndromal abnormality. Therefore if a boy is castrated prior to puberty, at seven or eight, the secondary sex characteristics will not appear. There will be no penile enlargement, no facial hair and no growth of muscle. The development of female characteristics such as pelvic enlargement and breast growth will depend on the balance between the normal male production of small amounts of oestrogen and testosterone from the adrenal glands. Some castrati would have grown breasts and others would not. What they would all do however is develop a female distribution of adipose tissue on the buttocks, hips and thighs.

Effect of castration on the voice

But what was important for the voice, and therefore for a castrato's future, was what happened in the larynx. At puberty three major changes occur in the larynx. The most important, and most obvious, is that in the male, the increase in testosterone creates bigger muscles. The reason that boys become bulkier and stronger than girls is this creation of muscle bulk. One of the most obvious sites of increased muscle is in the larynx. The increased muscle bulk is perfectly formed and there are the correct number of nerve endings to allow complete control of the voice. Basically the weight of the muscle of the vocal cord is doubled. This does not take a huge amount of growth to accomplish because the starting weight of the cords is similar to the weight of a quail's egg. The effect of doubling the weight is however dramatic. If we recall the formula, frequency = tension/mass, then it will be obvious that as the mass of any vibrating structure increases the frequency drops. So after puberty, when the cords vibrate, the male voice drops by an octave.

The second change is that the thyroid cartilage changes shape. It becomes not only a little longer in males but has a sharper 'front'. In contrast, a girl's thyroid cartilage becomes slightly larger but also becomes rounded at the front and so does not stick out in the neck. The male thyroid cartilage is like the bow and the female like the stern of a boat. This has an effect on the way the cords meet.

In this cartilaginous framework, the thyro arytenoid muscles become bulkier and heavier. Since the cartilage is getting 'sharper' the cords tend to meet along their entire length. A girl's thyro arytenoid muscle becomes only marginally heavier, not enough to audibly change the pitch of the voice. The shape within the thyroid cartilage is however slightly changed. Since the thyroid cartilage becomes more rounded the cords do not meet completely at the back and in later years when growth has stopped this gives most girls a 'breathy' quality to the voice.

The final thing that happens is that the larynx goes lower in the neck. Whether this is due to differential growth between structures in the neck and the chest is unknown, but the effect is important. The distance between the vocal cords and the lips increases in males. This means that the length of the resonating chamber becomes better adapted to the new lower frequency that will be produced from the heavier thyro arytenoid muscle.

In a castrato, none of these male changes occur. There is no increased weight of muscle, the thyroid cartilage does not sharpen and the length of the resonating tract stays short to suit the still high frequency that will be produced from the vibrating cords.

Changes in lung volume are probably as important as what happens in the larynx. After puberty there is a growth spurt in both sexes. It is not long-lasting in girls because the oestrogen produced from their now functioning ovaries tends to slow and stop bone growth. Pre-pubertal girls who are embarrassed about their height, especially in relation to small boys, stop growing and are usually passed by the boys who continue growing until their late teens. So without ovaries, castrati continued to grow and were tall people. This meant that they had much bigger lungs and rib cages than females which provided them with a larger reservoir of air and more power. Farinelli, about whom a film was made, could sing a line without a break for over a minute. This is not just due to lung size, but to more intercostal muscle with more neural control.

The castrati voice thus differed from the male voice in its lightness, pitch and flexibility, and from the female voice in its power. It was said that the castrati voice embodied the trinity of male, female and child.

When the sound engineers involved in the Farinelli film were trying to synthesise a castrato voice they sampled a female soprano and a male alto. They digitally inteweaved these samples to produce a sound that none of us had ever heard, but one that was almost certainly correct.

Castrati in society

The entertainment industry in the eighteenth century coped with women better than the Church and by the middle 1700s women were singing in theatres. It could be argued therefore that castrati had had their day. But at this point they were at the height of their popularity and they lasted another 100 years.

This popularity was reflected in their earning power. The successful ones made money that would be coveted by any present-day pop star. Why they were even more popular in Calvanistic northern Europe than the Catholic south remains a mystery but that was where the 'big' money evidently lay. Caffarelli was paid £1,000 for a season in England and Farinelli, Sensino and Cuzzoni, £1,500. The £2,500 paid to Velluti by Queen Christina of Sweden in 1715 would be the present-day equivalent of £4 million for a season.

If we judge castrati by present-day standards they would be freaks. There is no established place in our society for people of cross gender. The odd 'personality' who displays these characteristics may be accepted but they are 'one-offs'. Two and three hundred years ago there was a place for cross genders. There was a niche in society for them and by and large they were accepted for what they were and the successful ones adulated.

While the French would talk about 'eunuchs', 'cripples' or 'capons', the Italians used terms such a 'musico' or 'virtuoso'. In France, when they were told that people pitied them, Carestini and Salimbeni, burst out laughing – perhaps all the way to the bank!

What is less certain is how they regarded themselves.

The brain is genderised *in utero* and it is something that will not change. If this process is prevented in a male rat brain, they will have male characteristics but will behave as females. In the

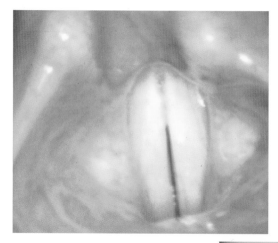

1 Vocal cords closed. The arytenoids are at the top of the picture and the cords are the smooth white bands.

2 Vocal cords open. Between them you are looking down the windpipe towards the lungs.

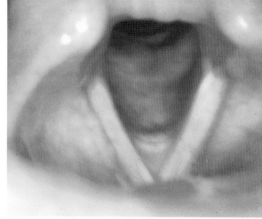

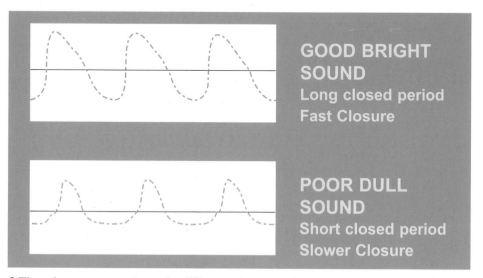

GOOD BRIGHT SOUND
Long closed period
Fast Closure

POOR DULL SOUND
Short closed period
Slower Closure

3 These laryngograms shows the difference in mucosal action between a trained and untrained singer. Each cycle represents one of hundreds of vibrations per second.

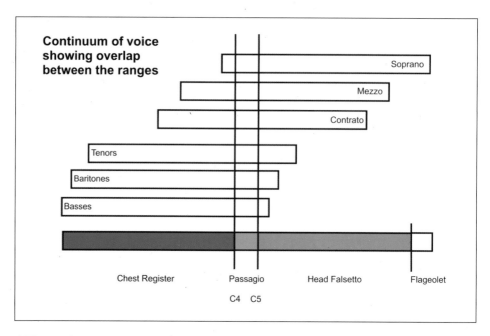

Continuum of voice showing overlap between the ranges

Soprano

Mezzo

Contrato

Tenors

Baritones

Basses

| Chest Register | Passagio | Head Falsetto | Flageolet |

C4   C5

4 The continuum of the voice shows how the male and female voices overlap. You can see that no matter what the voice type, every professional singer can sing the 'F' above middle 'C'.

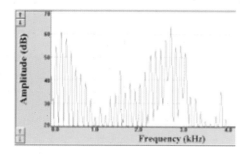

5 The acoustic signal from a trained singer shows greater number of harmonics with a peak at around 3kHz. This is what makes a voice sound bright and makes it capable of being heard unamplified over a big orchestra.

6 The acoustic signal from a non-singer shows harmonics that are less than those of a trained singer with no concentration at 3kHz. This means that although the voice may sound loud it will not project.

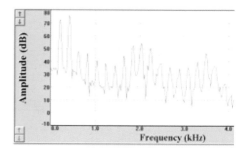

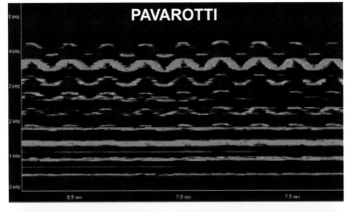

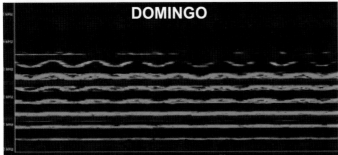

Spectograms of **7** Pavarotti and **8** Domingo singing the same note. Pavarotti, a natural tenor has one band of resonance just above 3kHz while Domingo, a natural baritone who sings tenor, produces many more harmonics that makes them sound different. Their vibrato pattern is also different, with (on this note) Pavarotti having a wider pattern.

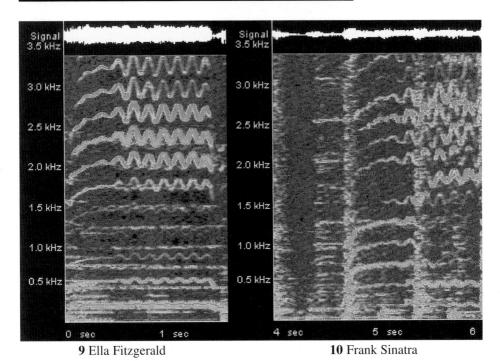

9 Ella Fitzgerald   **10** Frank Sinatra

Spectograms of Ella Fitzgerald and Frank Sinatra showing good harmonic production and resonance at around 3kHz with regular patterns of vibrato.

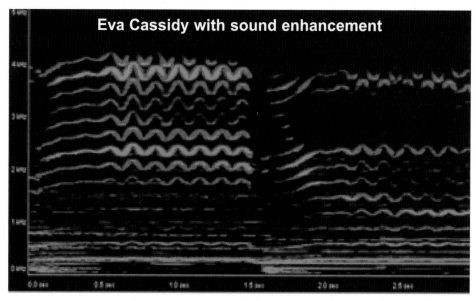

Eva Cassidy with sound enhancement

11 This is a spectrogram of Eva Cassidy singing the 'where' syllable of 'Somewhere Over the Rainbow'. The strong parts of the voice display themselves in red while blue is the non resonant part. The frequency at which she is singing is shown by the lower red line but this cannot be heard by the human ear. She resonates at just above 2kHz. Her vibrato is seen as the regular wavy line on the higher partials; it is regular in frequency and amplitude so she doesn't sound 'wobbly'.

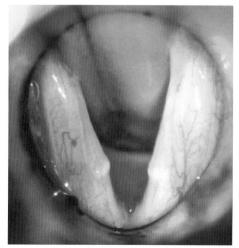

12 Vocal Nodules.

13 Vocal Cord Polyp.

1950s a Harvard psychologist, John Money, studied a small cohort of boys who had lost their genitals in accidents. His view was that it was better to go the whole way and remove the remaining genitals and bring them up as females. Twenty years later this group were followed up by a Canadian psychologist who found that they had all had dreadful lives because they could not fit in. They could not change their behaviour drive and many had attempted suicide.

I'll bet Will Young and Gareth Gates are glad they weren't born a few hundred years ago! Becoming a manufactured star by TV is a lot easier.

The difference between castrati and counter tenors

The difference between a counter tenor and a castrato is that the counter tenor went through puberty, has muscle mass in the vocal cords, has male secondary sex characteristics and has a larynx that is in the low male neck position. The sound is that of a female contralto and even on occasion into the soprano range but with a different range of singing voice. It is a voice that has become popular since the 1980s with the acceptance of the gender blurring brought to the fore by various pop groups. There is an added interest in hearing a male sing like a female. Recordings by Michael Chance, David Daniels and Andreas Scholl sell very successfully, and their availability has allowed a revival of the operas of Handel, Gluck and Purcell.

Counter tenors make their special sound in two completely different ways. If they didn't 'trick up' the use of the vocal cords then their voice would be that of a normal male tenor or baritone. Their speaking voices are unmistakably male. The frequency produced from the vocal cord vibration depends on the weight of the vibrating portion. Females do not have as much muscle weight as males and so the frequency that they produce by vibrating the *whole* cord is higher than when a male vibrates his *whole* cord. So if a male wants to vibrate a lighter vocal cord he can do it in one of two ways.

The first way is to make the cord thin by tightening the thyro arytenoid and then only to vibrate half of the cord! The effect is to translate only half of the muscle weight into the formula *frequency = tension/mass*. In other words they vibrate only half the muscle

87

under greater tension, the frequency doubles and the sound becomes an octave higher. They do this by using only parts of the muscles. All muscles are not made in exactly the same way. They are generally the same but if some fibres are stronger than others and if some angles of fibres are slightly different from others then the structure they move will be affected. Think of the effect on a puppet if the operator slightly alters the position of the strings.

The two muscles involved in this 'trick' movement are the crico thyroid on the outside of the thyroid cartilage and the posterior crico arytenoid muscle on the back of the cricoid. The crico thyroid muscle has two segments – one pulls the thyroid forwards and another tilts it down (page 14). If someone has the part that pulls the thyroid forwards better developed than the tilting part then they can lengthen the cords while at the same time keeping them on the same plane. The posterior cricoarytenoid muscle is attached to the back of the cricoid and usually opens the vocal cords by rotating the arytenoids apart. If however there is a well-developed vertical set of fibres as opposed to the usual oblique set, then the person so endowed will be able to lift the plane of the vocal cords by tilting the arytenoids backwards. Although a chink appears at the back of the larynx, the air escape is minimised and not heard. At the same time the back of the glottis opens because the vocal cords are pulled apart and there is a chink. While some air escapes and there is the attractive female breathy quality, the main purpose of pulling the backs of the cords apart is to reduce their vibrating length, thus producing a higher frequency.

The second way of producing this curious sound is by using the whole cord but halving the weight of vibrating muscle. This is essentially what is done in the music theatre and the pop voice when singing falsetto. The vocal cords are used like a whistle. There is no vibrating mucosal wave and the pitch is altered by skilfully changing the length of the vocal cords. To do this requires a hyper-elastic vocal ligament and also a very lax ligament at the joint where the thyroid articulates with the cricoid. Stretching the cord like this effectively halves the amount of muscle weight that is vibrating and it gives the same effect as the first method, which is to use only half the available muscle. Singers who can do this are 'vocal gymnasts'; in the same way as a gymnast can put their joints through an abnormal range of movement so do these singers do the same in the larynx.

Since this method abolishes the mucosal wave such singers do not produce the usual quantity of harmonics. Their saving grace is that they don't need to because the fundamental frequency is always above 1.8 kHz and so, like the soprano, the fundamental frequency that they're singing only needs to be doubled and they arrive at the magic 3 kHz for projection. Some do this by adding the first formant but some do it by producing enough higher partials to create a third formant at 3 kHz; and it is this difference that makes singers in this range sound different. Those with a first formant only will have a warm voice but those who can produce a third formant will have a bright voice.

With both of these techniques it's necessary to raise the larynx in the neck in order to shorten the vocal tract and create the correct length for resonance and projection.

Boy trebles

Many great male singers were once outstanding boy trebles. But on the other hand many outstanding boy trebles never sing professionally after puberty. The range of a boy treble is again governed by the vibrating muscle mass. There are no 'trick' movements and the sound that comes out is governed by the fundamental sound that comes from the vocal cords and the resonance that is created by the length of the vocal tract. Add to this some basic musicality and you have a 'gift of God'. In other words, everything works and it's usually by serendipity.

Boy trebles sing in the soprano range but the voice sounds quite different from both a pre-pubertal female voice and an adult soprano voice. The reason for the difference in sound quality is twofold. First, boys have a particular resonance at 5 kHz which is not heard in any other voice. It is this resonance that gives the piercing quality that sounds so well in church music, especially when it is amplified by the cathedral environment. It would however be unacceptable in a professional soprano singing unamplified. Second, boys can produce a high subglottic pressure from their relatively smaller vocal tracts through their lung airflow.

The interesting question is why more outstanding boy trebles don't go on to be outstanding tenors or baritones. As a boy treble, Aled Jones had a voice of outstanding beauty but his adult singing voice is that of a pleasant light baritone. This is because he sings as an adult as he did as a child. His spectrogram shows that when he sang as a boy treble he showed the typical vibrato-free high range with enhancement towards 3–5 kHz. His spectrogram as an adult, singing exactly the same note an octave down with a light baritone voice, shows that his voice use has not progressed to a full adult male singing voice with a developed passagio. He still uses the thin edge of the vocal cords that he used as a boy treble and so there is not enough mucosal activity to produce harmonics that can be gathered at 3 kHz and used for projection. In other words, he's taken the line of least resistance and sings in the 'comfort zone', which is however very pleasant.

9

The Classical Pop Stars

Music theatre followed operetta, which in turn followed 'volksopera'. In the UK, music theatre in the Twenties and Thirties was monopolised by the shows written by Noel Coward and Ivor Novello. The voice style was operatic for one simple reason – lack of amplification. The only way to project a voice over an orchestra was to use operatic technique with the voice producing big harmonics due to fast mucosal closure. This produced a ringing voice that we, today, would think was 'corny' for the genre, but in the Twenties and Thirties it was the only way for singers to be heard.

Meanwhile amplification via microphones was developing but it wasn't until the Thirties that they became so good that single singers in a theatre could be heard above a band. And from then on there was no stopping solo singers and small groups. They put big (and expensive) bands out of business. So let's look at the technology that made modern pop music, amplification.

Amplification

The basic tool for amplification is the microphone. The first usable microphone for singing was produced by Western Electric in 1915. This first generation depended on the carbon transmitter which also produced a lot of added noise. Driven by the requirement to add sound to motion pictures in the mid-Twenties, the condenser microphone was invented and finally perfected by Georg Neumann. The ribbon or 'velocity' microphone was introduced by RCA in 1931 and became the most widely used microphone in vocal recording. After World War II the polydirectional microphone was introduced. In the Fifties the axial microphone became popular because it could be carried by the singer.

The principle of any microphone is that a diaphragm, which moves with the sound pressure, is joined to something that creates an electrical signal that can be adapted according to the sound required. There are two ways that this can be done.

The first is where the diaphragm is connected to a conducting plate to form a capacitor or a condenser. This vibrates with the sound and varies the charge which goes in and out of the capacitor. This type of mike is used in recording studios and can be very large. The larger the diaphragm the larger a sound field that is collected and with the superb signal-noise ratio there is minimal background noise.

The second type of microphone is where the diaphragm is connected to a coil which moves in a magnetic field producing an electrical charge. With this type it is possible to have a more robust and stronger design, so this is most used in stage work.

In the Fifties and early Sixties (including the early productions of *Jesus Christ, Superstar*) microphones were hung from the top of the stage and were also placed behind the footlights. The shape of the housing of a microphone dictates where the sound is heard and so a fixed stage mike can be constructed only to receive sound from one side. The Sixties musical, *Hair*, involved a lot of dancing and movement. The original cast had hand-held microphones with cables and so the choreography had to cater for this and it was as important for the performer to know which hand to hold the mike in as it was to remember the dance steps.

The next development was the radio mike which made life a lot easier since there were no cables or leads. These still had to be held in the hand but which hand was not so much of an issue.

In the Seventies it became possible to miniaturise diaphragms and coils. This allowed microphones to be invisible and to be sewn into the costumes. The next generation of miniaturisation led to mikes being small, flat objects that could be stuck to the head. Common sites were above the ear or under the wig line, if one was worn. The principle was to get the mike as close to the mouth as possible. These allowed the sound engineer to modify the sound as the music required but there were two main problems with radio mikes worn like this. The first was that on occasion the frequency clashed with that of the police, and the singer could pick up police messages in the middle of a song. The second was that the singer could not hear themselves and perhaps, thinking that they were too soft, especially if there was a loud electronic accompaniment, they might start to shout instead of sing.

An important part of stagecraft is to remember to switch the radio mike off when offstage. There was one famous occasion when an opera singer was doing an outdoor concert with a radio mike, and, not being used to the discipline of switching off and on, he forgot. The audience then had another singer's performance interrupted by the sound of urine running, followed by a toilet flushing!

At the present time most artists wear headsets that have an earpiece. The advantage of this arrangement is that the singer can hear themselves and since the mike is at the mouth, the sound can be better controlled. The problem, however, is that they are incredibly ugly.

Big band singers

From the Thirties to the Fifties the big bands were the fashion. They played primarily for dancing in big ballrooms, but got a much wider audience because of radio, and to a lesser extent, records. They all had singers, and the repertoire consisted of songs that all had the same format with mind-numbingly boring harmonic structures. In the main these were 'written to order' – in the same way that, 30 years later, they were in Motown. The sales were in sheet music form, which in turn brought requests to radio stations for playings, which paid copyright money to the music publisher. It was a very successful business that was not threatened by any other music form and which from time to time got an injection of new talent and material from the cinema.

The big bands had their fan bases, their charismatic leaders and their signature tunes – a concept that seems so banal now, but was an important bit of knowledge for every teenager in the Forties and Fifties. They were the style, dress and fashion leaders of the time and took over from the now boring jazz bands. There was also still strict segregation in the American music industry and the big bands reflected this.

The singers were too numerous to mention and it is doubtful if, apart from Frank Sinatra, anyone could bring to mind a singer who regularly sang with a band. At first, singers were hired for nothing other than to add variety to the band's repertoire. They sang with a reedy chest voice and most have long since departed with no record of their achievements remaining. Rudy Vallee was typical of this genre. Mass record purchasing was still a long way off and most of these singers depended on word of mouth popularity and had to suffer the drudgery of touring vast distances, night after night, to ballrooms all over the United States.

Frank Sinatra was one of the first to develop a solo career away from a big band. His much publicised release from his Tommy Dorsey contract associated him with the Mafia for ever after. He developed his career, not only because of his outstanding musicality, diction and appearance, but also because the post-war years saw a huge change in the making and marketing of records. This was not only in the United States, but worldwide, because the rest of the world, during the war, had been exposed to US Army radio stations playing 'American' music.

There was also the cinema, which in the Forties became the premier entertainment medium. This was the way that Bing Crosby became a star, but he too had an underlying musicality, diction – and a well designed 'wig'.

The record industry was also developing techniques of distribution that got world wide publicity for a generation of 'crooners'. They sang romantic ballads with a baritone voice in the chest register, articulating well so that the words could be heard. The music was essentially an accompaniment and was not meant to intrude at all. Joining Sinatra and Crosby were Dean Martin, Perry Como, Frankie Lane and many others.

There was a parallel group of female singers who mimicked the style with either contralto-range songs if they were seriously romantic, or high 'girlie' voices in the head registers. Doris Day, Rosemary Clooney and Peggy Lee were typical of that group. Banal lyrics to banal harmonies expressing the joy of new love or the rejection of former loves dominated. But this repertoire did not allow belting or twanging largely because it was not in keeping with the musical style.

Singing the standards

Tunes that were written in the post-war period were as blatantly commercial as the present-day *Pop Idol* or *Fame Academy* 'contests'. Nearly every one would be guaranteed a short term success. The annual Christmas song is a good example. It could be written to order and would have seven or eight ingredients. It had to be sung by a well known crooner, it would have to have some children's voices, some sleigh bells, church bells, seasonal references to love, the word 'Santa', some nostalgia and a key change in the third verse!

The Hit Parade and the Top Twenty were invented as a way of focusing people's attention on what other people were buying (and by implication that they should also). Radio was used to get the tunes heard many times a day all over the world. Paralleling the record sales were the sales of sheet music which gave access to the words. If someone wants to learn the words of a song from a record, disc or tape nowadays they can play it over and over. The only records available in the Forties were 78 rpm shellac discs that had a finite life and any careless replacement of the needle would damage the groove and insert an irritating 'click'. It was cheaper to buy the music!

Some of the tunes written from 1930 to 1970, however, were seriously better than others and maintained popularity after they had fallen from the Top Twenty. These became known as 'standards' and formed the basis of the repertoire of great singers such as Ella Fitzgerald and Frank Sinatra. Most were composed by Cole Porter, George Gershwin, Richard Rodgers, Jimmy McHugh, Billy Strayhorn, Neil Hefti, and dominating the Seventies, Hal David and Burt Bacharach.

Introduction of Rock 'n' Roll

When the film *The Blackboard Jungle* arrived in Fifties Britain it proved to be the start of a musical revolution. Bill Haley and the Comets moved and sounded unlike any previous white musicians. They were bringing black music to the white people, and that was reflected in their voices. Young British people had listened to both Radio Luxembourg and American Forces Network radio which played black music for black American soldiers based in Germany. But here it was 'for real'.

The way had been cleared for Elvis Presley when he brought this wonderful anarchy called Rock 'n' Roll into young British lives, and music was changed forever. And what was even better was that you could buy a guitar, learn a combination of three chords and imitate it. Elvis sometimes sang 'rough' and sometimes 'sweet' but not in the same way as the crooners did. He seemed to mean it more, and in 1956 his *Heartbreak Hotel* reached number 1.

Another comforting thing for young white Britons was Buddy Holly. He was gangly, wore big glasses and looked like the school swot. If he could play it and be adulated, couldn't we all? Two British rock singers, Cliff Richard and Tommy Steel both sang, sounded and looked American.

The Beatles, who learned their trade in Germany, mixed black rhythm with white melody and understandable and relevant lyrics. They still used combinations of three chords but used added notes that made it sound much more interesting, and in many ways broke many of the established rules of harmonic progression.

This period also saw the new breed of manager. Young like the bands, fans of the music and usually more sensible than the singers, they turned the music business into a youth culture.

Andrew Loog Oldham discovered the Rolling Stones playing in a pub in Richmond, Surrey, and realised that he'd found the perfect antidote to the Beatles, who were marketed as cuddly, polite and family friendly. The Stones were therefore sold as rebellious, sneering and surly – which was a bit ironic because the Stones were originally well brought up boys from the Kent suburbs, while the four 'scousers' had lived with drugs in Germany!

The voice didn't enter into any of this. None of them could 'sing' in a way that would make you want to actually hear the beauty of the sound they made. The voice was merely part of an overall image. The heart was a more important muscle than the diaphragm! What they were singing about wasn't an act – it was for real.

What Bob Dylan and Jimi Hendrix were singing about was real, and a whole generation could relate to it. When LSD was introduced to the UK, it was at first quite legal, and access to marijuana was simple. As drugs had freed the original bebop jazzmen from the confines of harmony and structure and given a hectic speed to their music, so did drugs affect the music of the Sixties. The artists were freed from many of their inhibitions and social pressures. Musicians became the spokesmen for a generation, produced 'Peace' records and became the spiritual and moral leaders to the young in their quest to save the world. To many of the listeners who were also on drugs it was also easy to believe in the dream.

After the Sixties

The Seventies saw the arrival of Elton John and David Bowie as well as groups like Genesis, Deep Purple, Led Zeppelin and Pink Floyd. In the UK the rebellion was against the government and society, and in the US against race discrimination and Vietnam. The Sex Pistols released *Anarchy in the UK* and at the age of 42, Elvis Presley died.

In the Eighties rebellion was against living conditions and hopes for the future. Margaret Thatcher had an effect on the type of music because youth loved to hate her. Youth unemployment and council estate life created anger that bred punk and electro pop. Technology was 'in'. The Eighties saw the beginning of multitrack tape recorders, polyphonic keyboards, electronic drums and synthesisers that made any sound believable. In the latter part of the decade fast computers with music software, MIDI (Musical Instrument Digital Interface), became available. This decade also saw the emergence of Madonna and Kylie Minogue, Bruce Springsteen and Michael Jackson as well as UB40, the Pet Shop Boys and the New Kids on the Block.

In the Nineties there was little left to protest about and that may be why pop was not as exciting as it was a decade previously. Rather than taking the music or the sound forward the industry was consumed with worry about the effect that the delivery of electronic music would have on traditional sales at record stores. The MP3 digital file format enabled audio files to be transmitted over the internet and copyright issues began to dominate the industry. When Napster software was introduced, there followed a legal case in which Napster was sued by Metallica for breach of copyright. New musical genres including rap arrived, where the words were produced in a non-voiced way; not sounding quite like the original non-voicers, Rex Harrison and Maurice Chevalier, but technically the same. There was also a revival of Country and Western music by singers like Shania Twain.

All of these groups and individuals could be described as original pop/rock artists, in that they all wrote their own material, they had something other than a 'clean' image, they were marketed in the adult press (*NME*, *Q*, *X-Ray*) and they were likely to work with a major label. Then the record companies found a safer way of doing it – manufacture their own pop stars. But we'll look at this phenomenon in Chapter 11.

10

Opera: The Long Road to Big Rewards

Very few young singers will wake up one morning and say, 'I'm going to be an opera singer'. Some may have seen a film or a performance that stimulated them to dream, but that is just the start of a long hard road.

The early years

Long before any thoughts of an adult professional life appear, the child will be noticed as having a very good voice. Bryn Terfel in his village in Wales was always good, long before he had even heard of Cardiff Singer of the World.

The ideal start is to sing in the school or other choir, while learning an instrument (preferably the piano, but failing that an instrument such as the flute that develops breath control). According to one of the greatest figures of English Opera, Anne Evans, singing lessons before the voice has developed are a waste of time. There is no agreement about the importance of the series of examinations available through the Royal Colleges of Music. They are certainly not as important for a singer as they may be for an instrumentalist. To show their musicianship however, aspiring singers who play an instrument will probably reach their Grade 8 by the time they are 13 or 14.

They will then try to get into one of the main colleges of higher musical education. These are the Royal Academy of Music, The Royal College of Music, The Royal Northern College of Music, The Royal Welsh College of Music and Drama, The Royal Scottish Academy of Music and Drama and the Guildhall School of Music.

In order to get a place they will have to go into competitive auditions with other young people who are every bit as good as they are, and who they will probably have met previously during the rounds of music festivals and singing competitions.

It is likely that the females will be younger than the males. The girls will probably come straight from school but most male singers do something else first. For example, Anthony Michaels-Moore was a soldier, Seigfried Jerusulum a professional bassoon player for 17 years, and Alfredo Krause an industrial engineer before making his debut at 28.

Some professional singers were small-time singers before studying seriously. Placido Domingo sang baritone with the family Zarzuela Company in Mexico, and Sherill Milnes was a dance band crooner and the voice of one of the all time great adverts – 'When you're out of Schlitz, you're out of beer'. Jusse Bjorling sang as a boy treble in the Bjorling male voice quartet when they toured the USA and Nicolai Gedda sang in a boys' choir in the Russian Orthodox church in Leipzig. Also, rather like rugby forwards, male singers need a few years after leaving school for their muscles to mature.

If and when they pass their audition for a music college or academy, singers will be allocated a teacher. Every college will have some teachers who are more famous than others, and of course all the students want the 'famous' one. It's a bit like a good amateur golfer wanting the same coach as Tiger Woods. That's a worthy wish, but they may do equally well with a less famous teacher at this stage. I'll say more about teachers later, but the relationship that a singer has with their teacher is a far deeper and more personal one than any surgeon or barrister has with their trainer.

Instrumentalists are able to practise for much longer than singers because their instruments are inanimate. A singer's instrument is their larynx, and muscles tire quite quickly. Over-exercise tired muscles and trouble ensues. So a practice session for a singer will be an hour at a time, made up of 25 minutes of singing, 10 minutes of rest and another 25 minutes of singing. They will know by their speaking voice when to stop, and there is never a temptation to go on too long because the sound becomes poor, and if they're smart they'll realise that they are harming their 'instrument'.

I have very seldom seen misuse or overuse muscle injuries in established professional singers, but that is the staple complaint of student singers. It comes about in two ways. Young people do not organise life in an orderly manner nor do they plan well. They therefore may not have done graded practice for a lesson, a master class or a performance. As auditions approach and agents arrive to hear them they may overdo the practice, often with incorrect muscle tone because of anxiety, and suffer an overuse injury.

Misuse injuries are more difficult to correct. Stress a muscle while you are using it incorrectly and you will damage it. One only needs to look at the appalling injury record of English fast bowlers in the last decade to see the sense of their authorities now employing a sports medicine doctor to work with the coaches. With a singer it's more subtle. The cricket coach can see if the bowler's foot is turned out too much at delivery, thus causing a strain on the groin muscles or knee. A singing teacher can't see the muscle action, they can only hear the result. If they have the student making a beautiful sound while using the muscles incorrectly then the outcome will be a muscle injury. Resting will cure an overuse injury but a misuse injury really needs a revision of technique and this in turn may mean a new teacher. This is difficult and traumatic for both parties and many young singers stop at this point.

When singers graduate after three years, they will have a good idea of their potential and their standard compared to their peers. They will know their voice type, will have matured their personality and will be beginning to have some idea of the sort of life they want to lead. Are they going to give up the unequal struggle, given the strength of the competition, and settle on teaching with occasional local performances? Or do they feel like entering the competitive professional world? If they are poor actors or don't have the histrionic qualities to be good on stage, then their preference may be for Lieder or concert work. But if they want to go into opera then their studies must continue.

The postgraduate years

If a singer decides to pursue an operatic career, then they will apply for a place on one of the new opera courses. There are many schemes for young singers, such as the Vilar young artists programme at the Royal Opera House, The Gerwood scheme at English National Opera, and the new Alexander Gibson Opera School at the Royal Scottish Academy. The opera houses in Paris, Strasbourg, Amsterdam and Brussels also have postgraduate studios that are linked to the house. Singers may also get a scholarship to study abroad and during this time may get small parts. Also during this period (usually two years of extra study) they will get to know the repertoire, study presentation, learn how to audition and also study the business side of the profession. They will certainly shadow someone and watch rehearsals in all the phases.

At the National Opera Studio, directed by the opera singer Donald Maxwell, there are places each year for 12 singers and three repetiteurs and there is a gross imbalance of applicants. Last year 120 females applied and less than 20 males. By the time a singer gets there, they will have a reasonable technique but they will continue to improve their passagio and resonance with lessons. In the National Opera Studio they learn about acting, style, group working and how to be flexible. They will increase their repertoire and will also be identifying the sort of roles that would suit them, both physically and vocally. They will sing in the main languages used in the major repertoire and be helped by three hours a day of coaching with a variety of teachers. They may have five different people telling them how to do the same thing, but this is real life in the opera world, where singers have to work with many directors and conductors, all of whom want things done differently.

The dangerous years

If a singer has very obvious and clear talent, agents or opera companies will be knocking on their door. This is a very dangerous period for a young singer. It's exciting, they've arrived, they're going to be a success, they're making some money at last, and the opportunities seem limitless. The danger is that they may be given too much too soon, and lose physical and then vocal stamina. Overuse muscle injuries are very rare injuries in the established professional, but they can occur at this stage in a singer's career. The vast majority of agents are very sensible but I have seen young promising singers that everyone wants to hear worked so hard and travelled so much that the original promise, and more importantly the original desire to succeed, have vanished.

Some European conservatories are very dangerous and are nothing more than 'opera factories'. Big roles, too early, have seen the end of many a promising graduate, who was initially thrilled to get a scholarship to an exotic European school. One of the 'casualties' who recovered was Mario del Monaco, who had a huge voice for a frail physique and almost had his voice permanently ruined by his first conservatory teacher. After it was rebuilt by Maestro Melocchi, he never trusted anyone again and did it all on his own – with a tape recorder!

I've seen several young British singers, new from college, being given unrealistic roles such as Susannah in *The Marriage of Figaro*, which means singing almost throughout the opera. I've also seen young girls being thrust into major Verdi roles, with the inevitable end point of rejection, accompanied by damage both to their voice and their confidence. So at this point the young singer's career is literally in the hands of their agent, who must get the balance between career exposure and vocal health correct.

If the singer is not one of the golden few who are snapped up and marketed, they will either audition for further scholarships, perhaps in America, apply for jobs in the permanent chorus of one of the major UK opera houses, or go to Germany.

There are a number of reasons for this. Germany is one of the few European countries where it is possible for a foreign singer to be employed. There is a long tradition of opera and most large towns have their own opera company run by the municipality. The singers are in fact on the same payroll as the bus drivers! All of this is possible because of generous government grants and subsidies.

There is however a downside. With traditional Germanic orderliness they categorise singers according to their voice type. It's called the *fach* system. Once a singer is pigeonholed it is difficult to come out of it and seek other roles. On the other hand it is a secure and comfortable position, it is salaried and there is a lot of opportunity to learn new roles and to perform, even if it might be considered artistically constricting.

Operatic life is harder for females than males. Firstly there are far more females who want to be singers and so the competition is fiercer right from the start. But more importantly there are far more jobs for men. Opera composers basically only wrote two sorts of role for women – heroines or maids. In any opera you have the principals, the chorus and a number of very minor parts right down to the 'twelfth spear carrier' – and all of these other small roles are for men!

103

Life in the chorus

What the majority of graduates who want to live in the world of opera do is to audition for an opera chorus. They will then have some sort of job security, someone else to organise their travel and hotels, a salary, and a pension when they're finished. It's an attractive career choice for a singer in their forties and while it might seem a 'dead end' for an ambitious young singer, this is not really the case. Initially they will be chosen from the audition for the qualities of balance that they bring to the chorus ensemble; they will not be chosen for their brilliance as a soloist. On the other hand, understudies for the more minor roles are chosen from members of the chorus. This does two things. First it allows the singer to learn the repertoire and second it may, from time to time, give an opportunity for a solo part and a chance to impress. Pavarotti, who was a baker and a primary school teacher, once sang in the chorus of the Teatro Communale in Modena.

Those who show promise may decide to leave after a few years and try for a principal career. They may have a 'lean' couple of years, but with a good agent they may well be successful because opera is performed in every country in the world. If, on the other hand, the gloss goes off the world of opera, or if the salary needs to be augmented, there are a few other areas where a singer can find work.

Life as a principal

Let's say that the singer has either been identified as a star singer from the start, or has matured and improved sufficiently for them to gamble on a solo career. By this time they will have identified their voice type and will know what repertoire they want to do and where they are liable to be successful.

Types of roles

The number of roles available for a singer depends on their voice type, their appearance and their acting ability. In the competition for male roles in opera, the tenor rules. Surprisingly, with females it's not the soprano, but the mezzo who rules. This is purely a matter of supply and demand.

As in every other walk of life you'll do what you're good at and work where you can get employment. You'll avoid the things you either don't like or find difficult to do. Similarly with opera singers. They will find a set of roles that suit them, that they do well and that provide regular employment. From time to time that repertoire will be enlarged, but new roles that are learned will be within the style that fits their voice and personality.

A Mozartian singer will have to learn a greater number of roles than a Wagnerian singer. The former might have to have a repertoire of up to 40 roles while the Wagnerian will live quite comfortably off 10–12. On the other hand, there are a lot of Mozartian singers, and far fewer who have the size of voice and the physical stamina to do a *Ring* cycle.

What a singer looks like is important. Unfortunately, this is more important for women than men. Since its inception, opera has gone through a number of phases. In the beginning it was the machinist who produced the special effects. Then it was the composer. The singer became the focus of attention when composers wrote roles for specific popular singers. In this period we saw the era of the diva, who in the days before surtitles, was not only incomprehensible but, usually, totally unbelievable. We have now moved into the phase of theatre. Surtitles, appearance and production have become as important as the quality of the singing.

A century ago there was luxury in the sets and the costumes that, apart from one or two opera houses, will never again be available. That was the true theatrical operatic production. Today, the theatre has to have more realism. Fat ladies dying of TB, beautiful girls falling in love with dumpy old men nowadays defies belief, and with the economies necessary in set and costume design, the *theatre* has to be more real. So sopranos have to be thin and beautiful and tenors tall, young and handsome. The sort of role that a singer learns therefore depends more on physique today than 30 years ago.

Tenors play heroes and lovers and so must have a certain height and attractiveness. They are generally 'good guys' but usually end up dead along with the soprano. In *La Bohème* only the soprano dies, in *Götterdämmerung* and *Aida* they both die and in *Onegin* the tenor dies on his own. One of the few times that the tenor has the last laugh is in *Il Trovatore*, when Manrico gloatingly tells the bad Count di Luna that he has just burnt his own mother at the stake.

Baritones play villains or figures of authority, so being overweight or squat is not a major problem. Baritones are more likely to be lecherous (Don Giovanni), whilst basses are paternalistic, wise and often have troublesome daughters (Wotan).

Tenors are young and basses old. Baritones are in between. Tenors are impatient, basses will eternally steer events from positions of immense authority. Baritones are the implementers who ensure that it all comes about. Tenors fight, basses scheme, tenors love and basses defend their daughters! Basses do not have the sex life of tenors on stage but they have gravitas and often speak on behalf of God or long-dead ancestors.

Acting ability

It's a lot easier to sing while standing still than when holding a heavy soprano, lying on a couch dying or wondering whether or not the shaky platform you're standing on is going to collapse. But acting is what opera is about. Maria Callas was never really in complete control of her voice even in the pre-Onassis days but she held audiences spellbound by the sheer drama in her voice and her movements. Today, there is a fairly wide spread of acting ability especially on the English stage, and one has to mention Donald Maxwell, a natural cabaret performer, whose Falstaff will live long in the minds of those who saw it.

Life on the road

The life of a principal is not easy. It's not just a case of going from luxury hotel to the Opera House and then back to the airport.

One of the world's finest Rossini tenors, Bruce Ford, kindly wrote this diary for me, which covered a few months of a typical year. It gives a good insight into how tough the life is even at the top.

It's 2 January and I reluctantly leave my family for an engagement in Spain. This involves a harrowing flight from Miami to Madrid during which the turbulence is so bad that 90 per cent of the passengers are sick. Since I was one of the few people who did not eat lavishly and drink too much wine, I escape this. Drinking alcohol on flights dehydrates and so I never do it as the flight itself is dehydrating enough. I stick to my large bottle of water and am sure to turn on my personal ioniser/humidifier which I wear round my neck. Every little bit helps.

Arrive in Madrid for transfer to Oviedo; hope they've booked me into a decent hotel. When I finally arrive it turns out that the hotel is OK and close to the theatre.

Rehearsals begin. The theatre is old and the dust is appalling. When was this place last cleaned? The heating is on and it is DRY which stirs up the dust. Same for the hotel. I buy (yet another) humidifier for my room, which I will leave behind when I depart.

Performances go as well as can be expected, considering the conductor is not giving an inch to anyone's chosen tempo. After completing three shows I leave for home.

As soon as I arrive home I come down with that cold that I have been keeping at bay since the start of the year, and I have to postpone my departure for my next engagement by four days. The theatre isn't very happy about this, but what can I say? My health comes first. At least this way I have time to see my family and wash my clothes – or rather, have them washed!

After six days at home I depart for Salzburg: it is FREEZING cold and I again deal with the dryness caused by central heating. The gig involves four concerts in four cities. So the fact that my hotel is lavish means little, since I'm leaving it in two days. We rehearse; the announced cast is not the cast that shows up; two of the singers have been replaced by other colleagues, some of whom I know. This is fun, as it means we go and have lunch together and hang out, which beats sitting in your hotel room by yourself. Unfortunately the Austrians smoke a lot and so hanging out in restaurants becomes less desirable after about 20 minutes. Meals are a rushed affair. This is a tough role for me so I have to be extra careful. In addition some highly intelligent person thought it might be a good idea to have a concert at 11am. Don't they know that tenors don't sing before noon? The concerts go well though and I go home satisfied after nine days and four cities.

I now have a leisurely six weeks to prepare for my next role. This is a new Handel role and it is huge, with 'a million' recuts, so it isn't like I have a holiday. But being at home means the living conditions are tuned in to my lifestyle. I arrange coachings five days a week to prepare the part with a pianist who lives close by.

The day of departure comes all too soon. Since I'll be in Florence for about six weeks I have a lot of luggage and won't you know it, Alitalia charges me overweight. They just don't understand; at this time of year you need both winter and spring clothes; then there are the scores, my laptop computer, my own pillow without which I don't go anywhere – and it all adds up!

The apartment we rented – this took many phone calls, emails and visits to the web to look at places on offer – turns out to be gorgeous, overlooking the old city, and it's comfortable too. Hurrah, we got it right! And I'll lose weight walking to the theatre which is quite a distance away.

Rehearsals are very hard work – the producer we work with believes in creating an opera performance drawing on his cast members' talents. But it is incredibly satisfying. I am exhausted every night though, so the walk home isn't always so appealing. But the theatre has a good canteen in which we eat well and cheaply; important in a city like Florence, geared for tourists and therefore expensive. As part of this engagement falls in the Easter holidays my family comes to join me. It is of course just great to see them but it also means that after rehearsals they expect me to spend time with them instead of flop in front of the TV or computer. I don't have much energy left – or do I?

The performances go spectacularly well and we are incredibly happy at the success which is the reward for an the hard work we put in.

I got ten days at home to unwind; this is mostly spent learning a Britten piece which I will perform in concert in Rome. It is a tough switch from Handel.

My family is again able to accompany me to Rome and we have a leisurely rehearsal schedule which means we have time to see the sights together. Guess what? Nobody told me the first concert was an afternoon one, which means I need a dark suit as opposed to the tails I brought. More expense! The concerts are enjoyable and so is visiting Rome. The hotel we stay in is lovely and friendly. My wife has her wallet stolen on the final day which puts a damper on things. We're usually pretty streetwise and careful but Rome has Grade A pickpockets. Fortunately my wife did not have her credit cards in the wallet.

Barely home I get a call to jump in to do a few performances in Berlin. Since I'm pretty tired I pass on this; I have work to do on a new role I will be recording this summer. Yes we could use the extra money but money can't buy you time! So I decide to have some down time before diving into the next project.

Soon after, I travel to Munich for a series of concerts of an old and well-known piece. It's an easy job although dealing with Germans is never easy. If I hadn't left here 12 years ago I might have had no voice left, because they SMOKE absolutely everywhere, even backstage, in spite of all the 'No Smoking' signs on display everywhere. This is also the case in Paris where I'm heading next. I do the odd 'standby' there, my bread and butter role and so it isn't very stressful. But I have a bad stomach flu in the middle of the rehearsal period and it confines me to bed.

It's now April. We've had a lovely relaxing holiday at our house in Florida and I haven't thought about singing. Back in London I've got to work on a new role for a recording and I've brought over my singing teacher, Mary Gillas, from Houston to help me tackle the difficult bits.

Two weeks' recording, with five days' rehearsals beforehand. Colleagues I've worked with before, a good time, but a killer role. But I think it works. A new record has come out which features me, and I get quite a bit of publicity coverage, including a 'record of the week' mention in one of the Sunday papers.

A small break in the schedule. I'm invited to go to a Grand Prix weekend; great fun but far too much smoke. Glad I don't have to sing after this.

A late addition to the calendar has me singing a Rossini role I haven't done for 15 years in a major house in Italy. It's a hard role and I'm not feeling 100 per cent about it so I have to modify some of the high notes, which doesn't make the conductor very happy. I spend four weeks in Venice and my family is able to join me for a week which is nice.

Then I go off to Monte Carlo which is an awful place to

be; there is hardly anyone there. People don't actually 'live' in Monte Carlo, they just claim residence in a tiny apartment (one of which I was able to rent at a reasonable price). The atmosphere of the town changes when the first performance rolls along since it is a Gala performance celebrating Prince Ranier's birthday. Most people in the audience look like extras in an operetta. What a bizarre place. But we go to meet the Prince. Afterwards there is a dinner given by an opera appreciation group consisting mostly of Germans. I have a horrible moment during dessert when it turns out that I am expected to sing for my supper. I decline but it gets a few backs up and the evening is ruined for me – we go home shortly afterwards.

A life like that takes stamina!

Rewards

Man works for reward. It can come as either money or status and recognition. It is a fortunate person who gets both. Successful opera singers may come into that category.

As in medicine, money is never ever talked about. You never actually know what a surgeon charges for an operation until a nanosecond before your jaw drops. I do not know what top opera stars are paid but the following describes how a contract is arranged.

Opera singers are paid per performance. There is a national agreement on rehearsal fees and for a non-salaried small part singer, and six weeks' rehearsal time may equate with one performance fee. A chorus member of the Royal Opera House will get about £40,000 a year, an established provincial company chorus member about £30,000 and a new recruit about £20,000. A moderately famous principal who has an international career will be away from home about six months of the year. He'll get about £3,000 per performance and will do about 50 performances a year, giving him £150,000. Out of this however he has to pay tax, travel expenses and rehearsal time.

The reason that Germany is not a popular place in which to accept occasional roles, is because everything including expenses is taxed at source so that the travel is done at a loss!

In recent years opera singers have been rewarded in different ways. Knighthoods have been awarded to Geraint Evans and Thomas Allen, and Kiri Te Kanawa, Anne Evans and Felicity Lott have been made Dames. A certain sign that, at least in the UK, opera singing is appreciated and rewarded.

Lieder singing

All well-known opera singers are in demand for recitals or concert performances of opera. There have been many illustrious singers for whom this is their preferred medium. Some singers such as Barbara Bonney and Bryn Terfel manage to switch between the stage and the concert hall with little difficulty, but others such as the late Kathleen Ferrier, Dame Felicity Lott and Ian Bostridge make this their preferred milieu.

The word 'Lieder' means 'art song' and that is precisely what it is. There is no scenery, no costumes or other distractions to take attention from the art form, and no conductor to direct and to cover over mistakes.

The recitalist stands alone on the stage with an accompanist and a piano. The voice has to paint the picture that the composer meant to convey to the listener. Before beginning a song the singer will think their way into the mood that they hope to convey and in this moment of magic the audience can be absorbed. When ready the singer will indicate to the accompanist. This is one of the advantages over the operatic setting: the singer is in complete control. They have selected the repertoire that best suits their voice and they have also selected the preferred key. The songs will vary in mood, speed and rhythm to avoid monotony in the 90-minute performance. The recitalist will sing of love, of rage, of humour and of sadness. Because they are so exposed they have to display superb musicianship and artistry.

Lieder music is largely written and sung in German, English or French with the main composers being Schubert, Schumann, Debussy and Britten. The singer has therefore to be very proficient in these languages, because what they are 'selling' is a poem, and as such, every word must be heard and understood. In opera, the words were written specifically for that opera and are largely secondary to the music and voice, especially now with surtitles. Vowels can

111

be altered at will in order to produce a more beautiful sound at the expense of comprehension. All Lieder on the other hand started out as poems that were subsequently set to music. The singer therefore has to concentrate on delivering the words as much as the beautiful sound that is the song.

The best voices for Lieder are the mezzo soprano and the baritone because they are closer to the speaking voice. To do Lieder, the operatic singer has to come out of the operatic voice. This means raising the larynx so that the sound is not so thick. Another reason for not using 'opera' voice is that the halls are smaller and the big thick voice would not allow the words to be heard and understood. It is unusual for people who do a lot of Italian opera to do Lieder. Maria Callas, for example, never performed Lieder. It is not unreasonable to think that the Italian equivalent of Lieder are the Neapolitan songs which speak, if more coarsely, of the same emotions as the northern European mode.

Most voices are suited for recital work except the bass voice. Apart from the Winterreisse, the songs written for the bass voice are nearly all of Slavic or Russian origin and few are about happiness!

Church singing

Since the Church was the patron of sacred music, it is little wonder that there is an enormous repertoire of Requiems, Masses and other sacred formats. It was not until Mozart that a composer tried to produce a composition and then hope to sell it. Composers like Bach were paid by the Church to produce sacred music by the week.

The Church is also the singing base of many amateurs whose singing will vary from untutored warbling in communal hymn singing to taking regular singing lessons and being the leading light in the choir. While smaller church choirs will take any singer willing to turn up for practice and for Sunday services, the major cathedral choirs will admit only after audition, and the standard of musicianship required is high.

Cathedral choirs are the core of English singing, and they exist in all the major cities. The voice type required for a cathedral choir is very different from the opera chorus. This is because the environment and the acoustic in which they perform are totally different from a theatre or concert hall. The surfaces are stone or marble, and there is an inbuilt resonance, so rather than the singer using a bright voice with internal resonances carrying it, they will have to pull back and allow the maximum effect from the external resonance. If a singer has a lot of internal resonance, with a concentration around the 3 kHz area that is required in opera, then the effect will distort the sound that is required for the cathedral environment and the type of music. It will 'cut a line', so to speak, through the sound.

One of the unique sounds of cathedral choirs comes from the sound made by boy trebles who have a peculiar harmonic enhancement at 5 kHz. This is a sound that is fast disappearing because it is no longer considered 'cool' to sing in church choirs, and the number of boys attending auditions are far fewer than previously. Most choirs now use girls for these parts but they have less power, no projection at 5 kHz and more monochromatic sound.

The biggest choirs will have perhaps six full-time male singers plus an organist who may also be the choirmaster. The full-time male singers will augment their usual salary with teaching and other singing engagements but their cathedral work comes first. From time to time other professional singers may be engaged for specific works. Most voices sound well in church, especially the lyric soprano whose tone is particularly suited to both the cathedral acoustic and the ethereal mood of sacred music. Emma Kirby is probably the best example of this. Flexibility will also add sparkle to the fast runs of *'Rejoice Greatly'* in the Messiah or the closing 'Alleluia' of Mozart's *Exultate Jubilate*. Normally the dramatic soprano has a voice that is too big for a cathedral but they are needed for the Italianate, quasi operatic *Stabat Mater* of Rossini or Verdi's *Requiem*.

Similarly, the dramatic tenor with a pronounced vibrato does not sound right for church music except that of the synagogue. The baritone is certainly the poor cousin of church music because very little is written for his range of voice. Even in a church choir the baritone has the choice of following the second tenor part or else the bass part, neither of which may ideally suit his voice. I don't know what church music has against baritones because even Verdi, who otherwise wrote all the great parts for baritones in his operas, never put a baritone part into his *Requiem*.

Choral singing

Choral singing is a very English tradition. The reason is that most other countries had a tradition of opera with the availability of singers and opera houses, but in England, until World War II, there was only the Sadler's Wells Opera Company. The core of singing was in the choral societies of major cities in the North and Middle of England such as Huddersfield, Sheffield and Leeds. They had world-famous choirs and many singers who went on to have solo careers, such as Kathleen Ferrier, started in a choral society.

In Scotland, there was the renowned Glasgow Orpheus choir, which, in the acoustics of the now destroyed St Andrew's Hall, sounded sublime. The Edinburgh International Festival, started in 1948, saw the birth of the Edinburgh Festival Chorus which began its life with Mahler's 8th Symphony under the direction of the late Arthur Oldham in 1963, with 1,000 people on the stage of the Usher Hall.

Teaching

Many young people will first be taught singing at their school. Those with talent who hope to go to college, or who merely want to get better for their own pleasure and for local operatic societies, will need a teacher who has experience and also some training in teaching and communicating. It's an extremely difficult job. An athletics coach can see what the pupil is doing. He or she can tell the javelin thrower to make a minor adjustment to the foot or elbow position. They can both then measure the result. The golf coach can make a minor adjustment to the swing, the stance, or the hand position and measure the outcome from the distance and straightness of the shot.

A rugby coach can get players to adopt correct body positions and can build up muscles in certain muscle groups by prescribed weight training. Both the coach and the player can see the result and the player has a clear idea of what they have to achieve. The cycle of video-study-train-perform-video goes on and on, until not only the muscle memory is engrained in the athlete's mind, but also the self-visualisation.

With the development of computer analysis of the voice, and

both real time and slow motion video, the last 20 years has seen the biggest advance in our knowledge about the singing voice since the Camerata were first meeting. Many advances have been of enormous assistance, such as allowing the teacher to see the pupil's cords move, noticing minor imperfections in the adjustment of position of the cord edges and the position of the arytenoids, seeing the mucosal wave slowed down by the stroboscope and getting graphic images of what teachers and singers have been 'hearing' all of their lives. But it hasn't changed what they always did!

A singing teacher has to get the singer to produce a good resonant sound that will 'carry' in a theatre full of people. Neither teacher nor pupil can see where the muscles should be, so it all has to be by imagery and listening. What I mean is this. The singer will sing a note. It won't be quite right but it's not bad. The teacher may want it marginally different – more open, more outwards, more sparkle etc. They will tell the singer something like, 'Pretend that the sound is coming out of the top of your head'. This of course is anatomical nonsense and both know that, but the efforts of the student to do the 'impossible' may well produce the sound that the teacher wants. On the other hand the imagery that is used between the two might not work. What works for one pupil will not work for all, because we all see things differently. Whatever the imagery used, it has to work, and if it doesn't, then it is time to change teacher. A good teacher will also talk in terms of 'feeling' the sound. If there is resonance in a voice, the singer feels a definite buzz somewhere in the head. It might be in the palate or it might be in the back of the nose, but the most usual place is in the so called 'mask' – the area behind the nose, eyes and forehead.

When I first heard the language and imagery of singing teachers I became an instant medical 'snob' and thought that it was dreadful that they didn't even understand the basic anatomy of where the voice came from and how it worked. My years of working with them have led me to a profound admiration of what they achieve by imagery. In fact, all my computers did was to tell them that they were right all along!

Singing training should be taken slowly. The singer is, after all, developing muscle, and more importantly, muscle control. This 'memory' needs time to embed in the brain. No damage will ever occur in the larynx if good, safe technique is learned from the start. All the problems with laryngeal muscle abnormalities that I have seen are due to a failure to use the muscle properly and then trying to salvage the situation with 'tricks' to 'cover up'. This is especially so in males. With stronger muscle and bigger airflow they can cover a myriad of errors in technique – until they are in their early forties when, as muscle power and control begin to decline, so do the errors show up more, and the voice becomes useless as a professional instrument. A good technique established in the early years is the foundation of a long career. A singing teacher does not need degrees, diplomas or certificates. It's not even important for them to have had a string of stars as pupils, but that does serve as a mark of eminence. What is important is the relationship that they can develop with an individual singer and their ability to communicate in terms of imagery so as to get that particular singer to achieve the best sound possible.

A singing teacher must know what a professional singer is expected to accomplish and they have to have had a wealth of experience of listening to and assessing performers. It is not surprising therefore that the best teachers have either been singers themselves or have dealt with singers as *repetiteurs*.

They must connect with the pupil's psychology in order to motivate and develop singing talent. Mary Gillas, the great American teacher, says, 'You must understand their thinking. You can only change the mind not the voice. You can no more tell someone what good tone is than tell them what velvet feels like or what chocolate tastes like.'

A teacher needs to be able to recognise and predict the potential of a student. Mistakes can be made. Maria Callas had the voice of an angel, but she never seemed to be in total control of pitch or vibrato. This may have been something to do with the fact that when she was a young girl living in Athens she had two voice teachers to whom she went at different times each week. One was teaching her to be a soprano and the other a mezzo!

11

Pop and Rock: The Road of Dreams

In the last chapter we talked about the classical singer taking time to develop the skills required for the job. But if a young person wants to be a singer and does not have the opportunity, the early ability or desire to go down the long road, there is another way.

No matter whether they wish to be a music theatre singer, a pop singer or a jazz singer, they all have to have some basic qualities. They have to have some sort of voice. When they emit a note it has to have some pleasing qualities and be far removed from a seagull's call. As we've seen previously, they have the ability to hit a note rather than sliding into it, and they have to be able to hold that note in tune and without 'wobble' for a few seconds at least. It's doubtful that someone without these abilities would harbour singing ambitions for long. They all must have a sense of time and rhythm. All classical singers will have an impeccable sense of timing by which I mean that they hold notes for precisely the time that the score indicates. To develop this skill into rhythm they have to be able to go the extra mile to vary subtly the time spent on each note.

Most modern music is written in what is called four-four time by which is meant that there are four beats in the bar. The timing and 'feel' of popular music is a little more complicated. Each of these four beats should be regarded as four series of triplets. So instead of 'da-da-da-da' the singer has to feel 'diddledee-diddledee-diddledee-diddledee', and the accent of the note will vary from the 'diddle' to the 'le' or the 'dee'. This cannot be learned other than by hours of listening to records, but even then some people cannot move outside the 'rules'.

Finally there is the question of accent. If a singer finds it difficult

117

to change their regional or social accent to American, then they should forget pop and jazz because it just won't sound right. Theatre music is different, but the singer must be able to mimic various social and regional accents other than their own, and also to sing with clarity in English.

Getting started as a theatre singer

Ten times more girls than boys want to go into musical theatre. They know what they want to achieve while in their teens at school, and will sing in local and school productions, all the while taking lessons. Most will try to get funding to transfer to a theatre school where not only will they continue with their GCSE subjects but they will learn singing, acting, dancing and stagecraft. There are dozens of theatre schools in the London area and the list is available on the National Conference of Drama Training website.

Some hopeful theatre singers, especially if they live far from London, will finish normal school and apply for a year or so at a theatre school, or do a three year degree course at a college of higher education. To be realistic however, if a young person wants to go on to the West End stage then they have to go to a theatre school in or around London. Next time you go to a show, read the biographical programme notes and you'll see that well over 90 per cent of the cast has this background. Some singers may also move sideways after a classical training and might get an ensemble job or a start in TV.

In general, the hopefuls come out of the various courses or schools with an agent who will 'showcase' them. Having an agent is a huge advantage because if you show promise they can get you a private audition, which is a lot better than the open auditions that are advertised in *The Stage* newspaper. For these, some 500 or so girls and about 50 boys will turn up and audition for perhaps half a dozen roles. Each will get about ten minutes and they might be asked to sing jazz, pop, rock, musical theatre or even Gilbert and Sullivan. They'll get to sing about 16 bars and the chances are that they will hear no more and will move on to the next audition.

If a singer does get a recall they will be sent music from the score and will have to learn it, act it and interpret it in a way that

118

they hope will please the casting director. As they prepare for this, they will probably go to a singing coach who may guess how that particular director likes the songs sung. They may be recalled for further auditions five or six times and still not get the part. The directors are looking for a good singing and interpretive performance, but most of all a physical presence that is *right* for the particular role.

Not surprisingly, given the competition, there are those who will never get a part after leaving school or college. In fact, the majority of graduates from colleges and theatre schools end up never working in the profession.

Life on the West End stage

If a singer gets a part then they will get a contract for at least six months, and probably a year, if the show is going to run. It is a very hard life. There will be a requirement to do eight shows a week, which for a classical singer would be unthinkable. The fact that they use amplification makes it possible. There will be shows six nights a week with matinees on Wednesday and Saturday.

The usual contract will allow four weeks' holiday and 30 days' sick leave. If they're in the ensemble the singer will be paid about £400 per week. An understudy will get a little more plus an extra £100 per appearance as a principal. A principal in a show like *Les Misérables* will be paid about £1,200 per week but a big star doing a main part may well get upwards of £50,000 per week. Since a principal will have an understudy they can often get away with five shows a week.

Having signed the contract the rehearsals begin. These will take about a month. In the first week the singer will learn the music, get to know everyone and start on character work. By the second week everyone will have learned the score, which will then be rehearsed in separate pieces. There will be rehearsals for singing, for dancing and for acting, all with different coaches. At this point many singers bring small recorders in and keep practising at home.

In the third week they will still be in the rehearsal room and what are called '*stagger throughs*' begin. This is rehearsing the acting, singing and dancing in the right order and together.

119

In the last week they go to the theatre and integrate with the technical side, such as lighting, costumes and sets. The only dress rehearsal that they will do will be on the day of the show.

The West End musical stage is a youth culture. People work very hard, and do long and what most would consider unsocial hours. If they live as hard as they work then the life may well be short and merry because for the voice to work the person has to stay physically fit. Very few get into the drug and alcohol culture because they all know that the voice will not cope in the long term. Alcohol and drugs dehydrate, burn the throat, limit the vocal range and eventually cause loss of vocal control.

About two months before the contract ends a singer has to think about the next job. They and their agent will have identified roles that their physique and image are suited for, that their voice is suited for and that they have the necessary skills for (e.g. roller skating in *Starlight Express*). They will learn the songs and embark upon more auditions. Success may involve staying another year in another town in a provincial tour of the musical, or they may get back onto the West End stage. Once again it will mean getting some coaching about the way to sing the part and they may well learn to sing the songs in several different ways. To see the famous coaches such as Mary Hammond and Paul Farrington bringing different qualities out in young singers is truly to appreciate their very distinctive skills.

If the singer gets another role, well and good. They are back into the routine of eight shows a week, looking for future appropriate roles, learning the songs and then doing the rounds of auditions. If not, the bills still have to be paid and they have to get other work. Stand-bys are waitressing, bar work, selling programmes, handing out leaflets and doing make-up and hairdressing promotions. Perhaps you have in the past wondered why so many good-looking girls are doing these jobs? Their alter ego is on the stage! The boys will do demonstrations, programme selling, bar work, teaching or taxi driving. And they will continue to do auditions – and wish that they'd got a better agent!

After ten years, only 10 per cent of those who started out will still be in the profession. While this might seem hard you must remember that this is a world of youth and image. A 20-year-old girl is a more marketable product in the ensemble than a 30-something girl, and every year girls one year younger are attending the auditions. Roles are available for mature singers – but not in the ensemble!

Getting started as a pop singer

It's easy to start this journey, but the chances of being even moderately successful are about the same as a young footballer getting a place in a Premier League squad. The roadway is perfectly clear. You get some friends to form a band, write your own material, get some local gigs, form a fan base, make a demo disc and get signed up.

Let's take them one at a time. You should decide your line-up and get a group of likeminded and above all flexible people to join you. Their singing voices should blend and their musicianship, even if you're on a limited chord repertoire, should be at least moderate.

Writing your own material is a must. The majority of what you sing in the early days will have been recorded and made popular by a famous artist, but you don't get paid for that. In fact, through the performing rights society you may have to pay! The reason you have to write your own material is that until you do get something of your own noticed you will be just one of thousands of other hopeful cover bands.

To get known and to get a fan base you have to get gigs; and to get gigs you have to be at least as good as the other bands in the district.

You might get asked back to some venues. Your pals will form at least some sort of following, but what you hope for is a fan base that asks venues when you're coming back next. You might take a leaf out of the old Viennese opera house where singers used to hire what was known as the 'claque'; this was a knowledgeable group who scattered themselves throughout the theatre and at appropriate times made enthusiastic applause and shouts for 'their' singer.

If you're any good you'll get lots of gigs – and even get paid reasonable fees. From now on the most important person in your life is known as the A&R person. This is a very old post in a record company and the letters stand for 'Artistes and Repertoire'. Big companies will have scouts at the bottom who will report to senior A&R people who then may come along to hear the band if

121

the scout raves enough about them. Basically their job is to sign one or two bands a year for the company that they work for. Fewer and fewer bands are now signed like this because of the more certain way companies have of getting successful record sales with manufactured bands. It's more likely nowadays that you'll have to approach a company directly. This will mean getting a manager who is good with people. The skills you need from a manager are not related to music but to people; you are the product and the manager is the salesman. But the product is a lot more saleable if it has lots of songs rather than just one or two good ones.

At some stage a demo disc is essential and this can be expensive to produce. A professional album will cost over £100,000 to produce so that can only be done by the record companies. You however, must expect costs of at least £500 per song. On top of that you then have to get some decent artwork done, but your manager *needs* this if they are to interest A&R people in the group.

Before demo discs reach the company however they'll have travelled round local promoters, friends and journalists. It's a hard fact of life, but record companies will tell you that 98 per cent of demos they receive are 'dreadful' and only 2 per cent are worth following up. So don't give up the day job!

Manufactured pop

By the beginning of 2000 the science of marketing records had developed to a very high level. Now there was a new market of mobile phone owning 8–12-year-olds who wanted to be grown up. They were labelled 'sub-teenies' and they were targeted.

The fact that few new pop stars emerged in the Nineties, together with the fact that the record companies could no longer afford to take as many chances with groups or soloists, led to the manufacture of pop stars by TV. These performers don't write much of their own material, they are marketed in a younger press (teen magazines) and are mostly signed with the major labels because they are already best-sellers before they've recorded a note. And since they are aimed at the sub-teen or young teenage market, all the focus is on style and image, which has to be 'clean'.

Bands and singers become products. Girl bands and boy bands, are both aimed at the same market, which is largely young teenage girls. The first girl band, the Spice Girls, had been worked on for a year before their first record was issued. There had to be time to put the merchandising and the tour together. They represented 'girl power' and by and large it was not 'cool' for young males to follow them.

On the subject of merchandising it's instructive to look back on the terrible deals that the Beatles' manager, Brian Epstein, put together for them in America where they probably lost billions of dollars in unseen merchandising opportunities. There was in fact virtually no Beatles merchandising because in those days there was no way of handling it. Nowadays there is a greater profit on a Spice Girl tee shirt than on a CD.

The first boy band was New Kids on the Block and they were followed by Bros, East 17, Boyzone, Take That, Blue, and West Life. They shared the same image as the Spice Girls. They were clean, beautiful on TV, pretty faces in magazines, and looked good on stickers and bedroom wall posters.

After 16 the 'adult' market kicks in. All the time the teenager is trying to identify with a group that they feel is 'them' or at least what they would like to be. It's at a time when they're searching around for their own personality. And there is always a marketing man to help them find what they want.

There's a double edge to the rebellious but 'clean' image: it can be changed when the time is right! Artists can move to tattoos and body piercing and get a new market as well as taking along some of the old market. They buy the clothes that go with the band and the type of music.

Sometimes a spanner drops into the planning. The Spice Girls broke up earlier than they were meant to. S Club 7 got involved with a cannabis scandal that lost them their Pepsi contract and it could easily have ended the band. They now have Junior S Club 7!

12

The Injured Voice

In August 1980, *Corriere della Sera*, one of the main Italian newspapers, had a headline saying, 'Voiceless Pavarotti will not sing in Milan'. This was not the first time a concert or an opera has been cancelled but it was probably one of the few times it has been the main headline.

Opera singers cancel performances much more frequently than their counterparts in music theatre or pop, but there are a number of very good reasons for this. The most important is that they have to sing without the aid of a microphone and so they do not have the help of sound engineers. The second is that an opera is a lot longer than a musical or a pop concert and the singer must always be controlling the voice themselves. And finally, an opera singer's vocal performance is listened to by an audience whose main interest is in the quality of the voices rather than in the production or the libretto. Towards the end of a career, rumours of 'being over the hill' etc. may start from a poor performance and this has obvious financial implications. We'll say more about cancellations later, but this chapter is about the injuries that occur to the voice and cause cancellations.

Why the voice gets injured

For a singer to produce a good voice the vocal cords must accomplish three basic things.

First they must meet together in the midline. To accomplish this, the nerve to the vocal cords, the recurrent laryngeal nerve, must be intact and the message must get to the healthy muscle of the cord. If the muscle is damaged then it will try to meet the other cord but it might fall short of perfection and a gap might result. If they don't meet, not only will there be no contact for vibration and voice to occur, but air will just flow through the 'hole'. What you will then hear is a very breathy voice.

Second, the mucosa has to rise off the underlying muscle in order to produce the mucosal wave that is the source of sound. If it is stuck down then it obviously can't move and so there won't be any sound produced. The commonest cause of this is scarring but it can also be due to abnormal muscle tensions, infections or dryness.

Third, the mucosa must be 'clean'. If something is on the mucosa as it vibrates then the sound will be altered. This can vary from a little catarrh which produces embarrassing 'gurgles,' to serious lesions such as nodules, cysts and polyps.

So let's now look at some of the things that can cause these problems and what a voice doctor can do about them.

Muscle movement problems

The most obvious reason for the cords not to meet is that something has happened to the recurrent laryngeal nerves that supply their muscles. This is potentially serious. While it may be due to a viral infection from something like influenza or glandular fever, it is often the harbinger of a cancer of the thyroid, lung or gullet.

Let's look at the cancers first. It is unlikely that a thyroid or a gullet cancer will paralyse a cord without any other symptoms such as pain, neck swelling and difficulty in swallowing being obvious to the singer, so we can 'park' these. It is rare to get lung cancer without having smoked. I know of no opera singer who smokes today, but formerly it was common, with Caruso reportedly smoking 40–60 a day. It is quite common for lung cancer to present with loss of voice, and no other symptoms, because the recurrent laryngeal nerve on the left runs around the root of the lung prior to coming up to supply the vocal cord muscles. It can thus be invaded by the cancer before any other symptoms develop.

The commonest cause of the cords not meeting is overuse and muscle fatigue. In the lower part of the range, when they are relaxed, the cords may meet but in the upper ranges when some tension is needed, there will be a gap. The most important decision the doctor has to make is whether or not this is a misuse or an overuse injury. If it is misuse then it is 'back to the drawing board' in regard to technique, because, after a period of rest the problem will just surface again. On the other hand, if it is merely overuse then not singing for five or six days will allow things to settle.

Mucosal movement problems

As the air flows through the small gap between the vocal cords when they are meeting, the negative pressure draws the mucosa off the underlying muscle. The closed mucosa is blown apart by the now increasing air pressure and the cycle of opening and closing is repeated about 100 times a second in the male and 200 times a second in the female. The 'clicks' of the opening mucosa are virtually continuous and we recognise this as the sound of the voice.

In order that the mucosa is able to lift off the underlying muscle and ligament, there must be a free zone that stops it sticking to the muscle. There are a few things that can happen to stop this free flow of mucosa over muscle and thus cause loss of voice. The most obvious is scarring.

There was a time in the not too distant past when vocal cord abnormalities both in singers and non-singers were treated by an operation of stripping of the cord. In this rather barbaric procedure the patient is anesthetised, a hollow steel tube (a laryngoscope) passed through the mouth and into the larynx, and through this tube the surgeon would grasp the edge of the mucosa and strip it off the underlying muscle, in the same way as you would peel an orange. If the reason for the operation was that the mucosa was showing signs that might eventually go malignant, then it was, and is, an effective thing to do.

In some people the mucosa regrows, and the space between it and the muscle remodels. For a speaking voice the regularity of this remodelling is unimportant because the voice returns, but in a singer who needs a regular mucosal wave then any irregularity in the remodelling results in a 'wobbly wave' which ruins the singing voice.

In the most extreme example the mucosa will stick to the underlying muscle with no remodelling of the space and even the

127

speaking voice will be very gruff and breathy. Fortunately this operation is no longer done unless as a diagnostic investigation for cancer.

When you have a cold your voice often changes. First it becomes deeper and 'bathroom singing' gives you encouragement to sing for a living – and then your voice disappears for a day or two! When it returns it is weak and breathy for another few days before returning to normal. How does this happen?

Firstly your voice gets deeper because the tissue in the space swells with added fluid from the infection. This increases the mass of the cord, changes the impedance and gives you a lovely, deep round voice. You'll be able to reach low notes you didn't know you had with good quality. But then the infection stops the so-called minor salivary glands from working. These glands keep your throat moist and you have literally tens of thousands of them, each producing a little mucous both of the thin and thick variety. If your throat is dry there is no 'click' when the mucosal wave separates and thus no sound – you've lost your voice.

Your throat also feels dry and sore. While many sore throats are due to infection of the tonsils or pharynx, the majority are painful because they are dry – and the dry lining hurts! Inflammatory cells enter the submucosal space and take a few days to be 'mopped up'. During this phase the sound returns because the mucosa is working, but not very effectively, so you can't build up much air pressure (weak voice) and a lot of the air escapes past the cords (breathy voice).

Lesions on the mucosa

Probably the best-known problem in singers are what are erroneously called *singer's nodes* or, more unkindly, *screamer's nodes*. Telling a singer that they have this problem usually evinces a reaction which in anyone else would accompany a diagnosis of cancer. The end has come! I won't be able to sing again! No one will employ me! If I can't sing, my persona is gone! What's left in life?

Well it's not as bad as that. When I tell a singer this diagnosis, and pick them up from the floor, I tell them what *nodules* really are, how it happened and how to stop it happening again. Here's the story!

128

You might remember that the opening to the voice-box is roughly one third cartilage (vocal process of the arytenoid), and two thirds soft tissue (vocal cord muscle and mucosa). The only bit that vibrates is the soft tissue. As an aside it's also the only bit that gets cancer and apart from smoking we don't know how. Nodules *always* form at the centre point of the vibrating cords, and so the reason they develop obviously has something to do with the way the cords vibrate (colour plate 12).

There is an earlier condition that I call *pre-nodule disease*. All types of singer are aware of too much catarrh collecting in the throat. When this happens, the voice feels tired and the 'ring' goes out of it. It usually only affects a small part of the range and is more noticeable during quiet passages. When I look at the cords in a singer with this problem, where do I see the build up of the catarrh? Why, just where the nodules will form.

A little later I'll see a small whitish lump on each cord exactly opposite each other. At this point the singer will not only complain of the catarrh collection but also of a dimming and flattening of the sound, especially when not singing loud with a big airflow. If this is left untreated and undiagnosed then the singer will lose range as well as brightness, get hoarseness in their speaking voice and finally produce sound that is nearer Rod Stewart than Placido Domingo. It can get to that stage in amateur and 'club' singers, but almost never in classical performers, who do not sing with amplification and so will notice the danger signs earlier.

If the nodules are surgically removed at this point and examined under a microscope, they will look like ordinary 'corns'. And that is precisely what they are and what you'd expect them to be. The constant 'bang, bang, bang' of an unusual vibratory pattern will do to the cord what the 'bang bang bang' of a tight shoe will do to a foot.

The diagnosis frightens singers because they have all heard of someone whose career has been ended by nodules. What is not always realised, however, is that this is more likely to be the result of being treated by a surgeon inexperienced in the mechanics of singing.

Taking nodes off a cord is the last card in the pack. Less than perfect surgery will certainly turn a top performer into a non-performer. By less than perfect surgery I mean the old fashioned method of removing nodes which was to anesthetise the patient, fit the laryngoscope so it sits near the vocal cords, and with one hand holding this up and steady, the other hand takes a pair of biting forceps and nips the nodes off. Most times this manoeuvre is done perfectly well but if the surgeon bites just a millimetre or so too deeply then, in healing, the vocal cord mucosa may stick down to the muscle. If this happens, the mucosal wave will be lost along with the voice – at least for top performance singing – even though the speaking voice may well be normal.

If the singer has managed to find a surgeon who understands the problem and does not rush to the knife first, then they should be advised to cancel all engagements for about four weeks, telling the people who have booked them that they have glandular fever, food poisoning, or some other self-limiting condition. I give this advice because some people in the profession still consider nodules as a career-limiting condition and when the 'word' spreads the engagements diminish!

The first ten days should be spent resting the singing voice completely but talking quite normally. Since nodules are basically 'corns', not using the voice for a short period will allow the 'early corn' to regress and disappear, in the same way as wearing soft shoes can heal corns. Uncomfortable though it is, the singer must accept that it is a fault in technique that has caused the nodules to occur, and I send them back to their teacher (most professionals still either take lessons or keep in touch with their teacher) and hope that they can spot what has changed in their technique to have caused the altered muscle movement that has resulted in the formation of the nodules.

When I look at the cords with a stroboscope the abnormal movement is quite clear. Instead of a vertical and horizontal vibration I see a figure of eight pattern with the waist of the eight being where the nodules lie.

If surgery has to be done, then the modern technique is to use what is called *suspension laryngoscopy*. The laryngoscope is fixed in a suspension apparatus allowing the surgeon to use both hands. The surgeon will operate through an operating microscope that magnifies the cords 10–25 times. In one hand he or she will have microforceps to hold the nodule and with the other he or she will use very fine microscissors to cut off the nodule. In this way a very limited amount of mucosa is removed and the excision will not be too deep.

Nodules are not *always* bad. The sounds made by Louis Armstrong suggested among other things, nodules, and I doubt if Rod Stewart's exciting, distinctive sound comes from pristinely normal vocal cords!

Vocal cord polyps have nothing to do with singer's nodes. The reason that they occur is quite unknown. They can be due to a bleed, a degeneration of a piece of localised swelling, a viral infection, or rarely, benign or malignant tumours. They look like polyps anywhere else in the body but have no particularly sinister significance. They all have to be removed to exclude cancer (which they seldom represent) but also because the speaking voice is hoarse.

There is no reason why singers are liable to get polyps any more than anyone else in the population but if they do get them they should choose their surgeon wisely and make sure that they have the technique described above – microlaryngoscopy with suspension (colour plate 13).

Vocal cord granulomas can result from years of chronic reflux, especially during the night. Singers are more prone to this because they seldom eat before a performance and if they are careless with food, and especially alcohol, at bedtime, the back of the larynx can spend the night being bathed in stomach acid. The chronic 'burn' that develops can break the surface and look like a badly-healed skin wound. Granulomas are difficult to completely eradicate but may not be too disastrous to the voice because they are often away from the vibrating area.

If however they are due to trauma – and the commonest cause of this is an anaesthetist's tube – then they are liable to be at a more vital area such as the very front of the cords. It is not necessarily due to roughness at intubation. It may be due to too wide a tube being used, or in a neck operation, the larynx being moved frequently over the indwelling tube.

Most anaesthetists however are very aware of these risks and often use what is called a laryngeal mask when they are anaesthetising singers. This is like a face mask, but goes down the throat, fits the back of the throat tightly and does not require anything to be placed between the cords.

Vocal cord cysts are a relatively new diagnosis. They look exactly like nodules but the white lump is only on one cord. Before we

131

used stroboscopy with frame by frame video analysis of cord movement, we used to think these were 'one-sided nodules,' because, at the same time, we didn't realise the cause of nodules. Stroboscopy has allowed us to make this vital differentiation. A cyst on the vocal cord is just the same as a 'pimple' on the face: it is a blocked minor salivary gland.

At first hoarseness appears towards the end of a performance but by the next day the voice is normal. This is because cysts swell with the trauma of the vocal cords vibrating and settle with rest. In a short while however they stay swollen permanently and it is no longer possible to sing.

If a cyst is treated surgically like a nodule and cut off, the surgeon might be lucky and go just deep enough to remove it all and not scar the larynx. This however would be the exception. The worst possible scenario is if part of the base remains, because this leads to repeated recurrences and increasingly difficult surgery. The end of a singing career is probably in sight. You can guess that this has happened when a singer has 'nodules' removed by a reputable surgeon and then never sings again. Julie Andrews comes to mind.

Removing a cyst requires even more skill and steadiness of hand than nodule surgery. Under suspension microlaryngoscopy, forceps held in one hand pull the cyst and the mucosa away from the muscle while, with the other hand, the surgeon uses a long microscalpel to make an incision in the top of the vocal cord to the side of the cyst. The next movement is to continue this cut on either side of the cyst, keeping very superficial and gently lifting the mucosa from the surface of the cyst. It is now seen as a 'white pearl' lying on the vocal cord ligament. The surgeon then very carefully dissects the cyst from the underlying tissue, taking great care not to rupture it. The wall of a cyst is several times thinner than a grape skin and if it is ruptured then there is a high likelihood of recurrence because total removal of a collapsed structure may or may not be successful. When the cyst is removed in one piece, the mucosa is carefully replaced and fixed in position with tissue glue.

13

The Lost Voice

The worst thing that can happen to any singer is to lose their singing voice permanently. When this happens temporarily, they don't *know* that it's not going to be permanent until a diagnosis is made, and so a doctor who understands how they feel is indispensable for them. There are occasions when voice loss can be permanent and it is usually a major traumatic life event for a singer.

As we saw in Chapter 12, temporary voice loss can be caused by many simple conditions. Perhaps the most usual is the common cold that causes a runny nose and a bit of a sore throat. The voice may actually sound a little better, and if a singer sings with a cold like this then they'll come to no harm. On the other hand if they have the beginnings of laryngitis, singing an opera may well result in intra-muscular bleeding and perhaps permanent vocal damage. In this situation there may also be bleeding under the surface of the cord which could take over a week to clear. This is especially liable to happen if the singer has taken some aspirin-containing 'cold cures', because aspirin 'thins' the blood and makes bleeding more likely.

About 1 in 50 people with glandular fever get a temporary vocal cord paralysis but fewer than 5 per cent of these will not recover. There are many secondary long-term complications of glandular fever and my advice to any singer when this disease is confirmed from a simple blood test, would be not to perform until *all* the symptoms have totally gone.

Lesions on the cords such as cysts or nodules, which have not troubled the singer before can swell as a result of the trauma of performance so that the next morning the singer is voiceless. This is because the swelling on the edge of the cord has now reached a critical size so that it prevents the cords from coming close preventing the harmonics required for resonance being produced. After a couple of days the swelling goes down, the cords are able to meet again with no gaps and the voice might sound normal. But when they start singing the same thing will happen again. They need to see a voice doctor and perhaps undergo surgery or else a longish period of rest.

Surgeons and singers

I have always done my best to think of every option other than surgery for a singer. This is more than natural caution. The vocal cords are a singer's livelihood and persona. Any general anaesthetic for any operation carries some degree (fortunately very small) of risk and many operations on the neck or chest put the main nerve to the vocal cords at risk.

The riskiest operation is a *thyroidectomy*. To take the thyroid out, a surgeon must display and identify the recurrent laryngeal nerve on each side. A thyroidectomy is done in order to remove an over-active or cancerous thyroid gland: the surgeon ought to keep these nerves under direct vision, so that there is less risk of damaging them inadvertently. The paralysis rate due to cutting a nerve is less than one per cent in good hands but in a singer it's the more subtle changes that may be just as important. While the nerve may be intact and undamaged to the naked eye, internal fibres might be damaged from pressure and manipulation of the nerve. This might show up as a loss of two or three of the higher notes at the extremity of the singer's range, or an unstable passagio due to marginally different tensions in each cord.

On the outside of the thyroid cartilage is a small nerve that supplies the muscle that tilts the thyroid on the cricoid and lengthens the vocal cord: the superior laryngeal nerve. It is difficult to preserve this and any damage is never noticeable in someone who is not a singer. Adele Galli Curci was the greatest soprano of her day. This is the story, summarised from the *American Journal of Surgery*, of her thyroidectomy.

She was a gold medallist from the Milan Conservatory in 1905 – but in piano! She had virtually no formal training as a singer.

134

She was encouraged to seek a career in singing by the composer of *Cavelleria Rusticana*, Pietro Mascagni. She made her debut in America in 1916 and for the next 14 years was a star attraction in New York and Chicago. She retired from opera in 1930 and toured the world to packed houses as a recital singer.

She developed a goitre (a swollen thyroid gland). Dr Arnold Kegel, a Mayo Clinic graduate, had a practice in Chicago and specialised in doing thyroid surgery under local anaesthetic so that the patient could vocalise during the surgery; he felt that this gave some warning of nerve damage.

He operated on her on 11 August 1935. At several points in the operation she sang scales, and at the end sang part of a duet from *The Barber of Seville*. But back in the ward she tried her voice again. The nurse thought that it was wonderful but the diva described it 'as a buzz-saw hitting a rusty nail' She sang again with Chicago Opera in 1936 in *La Bohème* but her performance was described by one critic as 'pathetic'.

Unfortunately the surgical notes have disappeared and so we don't know whether or not Dr Kegel knew of the importance of the superior laryngeal nerve.

Galli-Curci dates the end of her singing career to the thyroidectomy but we will never know if that is true or not. But what is certain, is that her *recurrent* laryngeal nerves were not damaged.

The risks of thyroidectomy however are well known both to singers and surgeons, and nowadays it is certain that any singer having to undergo this operation will have discussed every risk with their surgeon.

Another operation that singers fear is *tonsillectomy*. It is very rare that this operation is necessary in anyone over the age of 20, but some students have so much trouble from tonsillitis that the operation is unavoidable. By and large a student is not known to the critics and does not have a public persona. Their resonance will change as a result of the surgery because the shape of the pharynx will be different but it will usually be a change for the better. Even a student should choose their surgeon carefully because if too much tonsil base is removed, the adjacent portion of the tongue gets scarred and elevation of the tongue base is compromised.

135

What a singer should *never* have is an operation for *snoring*. All these operations involve scarring and stiffening of the palate. This could destroy a voice for ever.

'Nerves', and the voice

An ear, nose and throat (ENT) consultant will, on average, see at least six patients a year who has no voice at all due to 'nerves'. The clinical presentation is nearly always the same. It is usually a young female. She gives a history of sudden and complete loss of voice. When she speaks, the lips move, but you have to strain to hear any of the soft whisper. Looking at the larynx shows that the vocal cords are set wide apart and no amount of effort can persuade her to make them meet and produce a sound.

If she is asked to cough however, a normal sound is produced and this clinches the diagnosis, for it shows that the cords are not paralysed and can move, even if involuntarily.

It is a condition called *hysterical* or *functional aphonia* and usually arises from mental stress. A few sessions with a speech therapist invariably cures the condition and the person has an absolutely normal voice again. It is however a condition that tends to recur if there are further traumatic life events

Singers are not immune from this sort of problem. Maria Callas had a well-publicised series of cancellations during her most troubled years. Linda Ester Grey, one of Scotland's finest sopranos, sang beautifully in the final rehearsal of *Turandot* and then refused to go on for the opening night. She never sang professionally again. Another Scottish soprano, Norma Burrows was singing Gilda to Dennis O'Neil's, Rigoletto. She said that she found that she just couldn't continue and gave up the profession for good.

Dystonia

The most destructive of the conditions that cause voice loss and permanent loss of career is *dystonia*. This is an ill-understood condition and takes many forms. While a handful of people are found to have associated neurological signs (and some attempt has been made to associate it with malfunction of an area of the brain

136

called the basal ganglia), no hard evidence is available to give this condition an organic basis at the moment. It can affect many parts of the body.

Schumann, who wasn't quite as good a pianist as his wife Clara, got dystonia in his hand. It went into a claw like state and he could no longer play. A similar position occurs in writer's cramp when the sufferer cannot hold a pen.

It is a condition that all golfers fear. It very nearly ended the career of the Ryder Cup captain, Bernhard Langer. In golf it is colloquially known as the 'Yips'. The golfer addresses a putt and 'freezes'. He cannot take the club back or move it forwards. When he finally hits the ball it is without control and is an incoordinate jab rather than a stroke.

The likely cause lies in the failure of part of what is called the myotatic reflex (page 21). When a muscle is about to move, a message is sent to its 'antagonist' (the muscle that does the opposite movement) to relax. If this message is not sent, the antagonist does not relax, and so the primary agonist is not only trying to do a movement but is trying to do it with the opposite muscle trying to stop it.

In the larynx there are two well recognised types of dystonia, namely adductor and abductor. Abductor dystonia is when the person has difficulty getting the cord apart; it is a very alarming condition because they cannot breathe and often end up with a tracheostomy. Fortunately this is a very rare condition. The commonest situation is where the person has difficulty bringing the cords together (adductor dystonia). In Chapter 2 we showed the two muscles involved in opening and closing the cords. If the 'opening' muscle fails to relax, the 'closing' muscle has great difficulty bringing the cords together. The result is that with a great effort the cords are brought together for short periods but any fine adjustment of tension or length is impossible. The person will therefore speak in very short monotonic phrases with a sound that resembles a creaking wheel. Some cases respond to intracordal injection of botox but there are seldom any long-term 'cures'. For a singer, it is the end of the career.

Lost voices

Voices can be ruined by singing teachers, by surgeons, and also by singers themselves. Here are some tales of caution all of which are reproduced anonymously with the permission of the singers.

JT was a mezzo-soprano with a future that held high promise. She left her first music academy after graduation and went to a famous singing teacher at another academy in the UK. He tried to change her voice to a contralto. He did this because he thought her natural voice was deep enough to cope with the contralto range. What he didn't know was that JT had been doing extra chorus work to raise a bit more money and had overdone things. He had mistaken vocal cord swelling and a relatively deep speaking voice for natural development rather than damage. He was getting her to sing as low as the C below middle C and while it worked initially she found herself unable to go up the range. She got stuck at the passagio. She had an excellent chest voice but at the passagio she came to a complete halt and could go no higher. She was marched off to a voice doctor who saw swollen cords but failed to close the loop and merely diagnosed these as 'bruised'. When we saw her, her speaking voice was perfect, but she had a range of no more than half a dozen notes, all below the passagio. We tested all the laryngeal muscles electronically by putting minute needles into them and measuring their activity. All the muscles were working but when she approached the passagio, instead of thyroarytenoid relaxing and 'handing over' to the vocalis and vocal ligament, it stayed tight, and in fact pulled the arytenoids forward so that they tilted down into the glottis. The thyroarytenoid had got so used to working as a bunch, it could not relax and allow head voice. We and other teachers failed to break this abnormal muscle cycle and so she had to give up her singing career.

A self-inflicted injury ended DR's operatic career. He was one of Britain's finest baritones and some of his roles were legendary. He was singing Escamillo in *Carmen* which is an extremely difficult role – too high for baritones and too low for tenors! At a certain point he felt a crack in his larynx and the passagio disappeared. Thereafter his chest voice remained good as did his head voice, but at the passagio he never quite knew what was going to happen and often only an uncontrolled 'warble' was emitted.

138

What we saw initially after the 'crack' was a mucosal wave which was different on each side at the break, and his voice yodelled rather than sang over two or three notes. He could get round the problem by producing a big airflow, but he could never sing quietly in that area again. What he had done was to dislocate the small joint that allows the cricoid and thyroid to rotate on each other thus lengthening the vocal cords at the passagio.

As explained in Chapter 2, the cricothyroid muscle has two segments, an oblique set of fibres and a horizontal set. The oblique fibres pull in such a direction that the cartilages rotate on each other and the cricothyroid joint acts as the fulcrum around which this rotation occurs. The horizontal part of the muscle pulls the thyroid cartilage forwards on the cricoid by partially dislocating the joint with some added ligamentous laxity. This is the way that some big muscular singers get into the higher voices through the passagio but it isn't a technique that is frequently taught. That night, during *Carmen*, DR, who is a big man, overdid it and probably breached the joint capsule that holds it all together through over-enthusiastic laryngeal lengthening.

RM was one of Britain's best Mozartian sopranos. She was singing at ENO and had a mild virus infection. She took over the role of the Three Hoffmanns, which is an enormous sing, and thereafter lost her voice. She did not sing again for three years because she could not cope with the passagio. What had happened was that she had almost certainly bled into her intra-laryngeal muscles. In 90 per cent of cases when this happens, the blood is absorbed and the muscles heal. If, however, for some reason the blood turns to scar tissue then the motor units are damaged. You may recall that using an equal number of motor units on each side was vital for controlled voice production especially in the passagio. Basically it took three years for RM's motor units to be re-educated.

14

Lifestyle Problems

Obviously, singers, being human, worry about the same things as non-singers – finances, relationships and their future. But depending on how you earn your living you'll have some specific concerns. Surgeons worry about their eyesight, pianists about their hands, 'personalities' about their appearance and singers about their voices.

No one else in the music industry carries their instrument within them apart from singers. Every other instrument is replaceable apart from a voice. In this regard, opera singers are exactly the same as theatre, rock and pop singers.

The thing that all singers fear are doctors who neither understand singing nor their profession. Being told just to rest is not helpful. Being given medication that dries the throat is unhelpful. Being offered surgical procedures without sufficient information on the risks to the voice is a menace. But it's a two-way thing. Most of my colleagues regard singers as an absolute 'pain'. They make a fuss about little things that shouldn't have got beyond a general practitioner. The medical profession as a whole has not been as supportive of performing arts medicine as it has of sports medicine. In 1992, the UK performed abysmally at the Olympic Games. The then Prime Minister, John Major, allocated a large amount of money for a Sports Institute and to sports medicine. Last year, the UK was bottom in the Eurovision Song Contest – the result was public scorn!

I have long tried to get Performing Arts Medicine established as a separate multi-disciplinary specialty in the same way as Sports Medicine, but have failed to interest either the Faculty of Occupational Medicine, the Colleges of Physicians and Surgeons, or the College of General Practice.

Most of what follows in this chapter relates to things that we all might do or suffer from. We all may smoke or drink, travel in aeroplanes, live in hotels, overeat, have allergies and grow old. All of these things are important to us but are of greater significance to someone who earns their living with their voice.

Smoking and drinking

These are the most damaging bad habits, but while very few opera singers smoke, many rock and pop singers do.

Smoking does two things to the throat. The first is to change the type of lining from delicate mucosa such as you see on the inside of your lip, to thicker tissue like the outer covering of the lip. Sometimes, over the years, the changed lining becomes cancerous. The second thing is a change to the volume of the vocal cords. They swell and produce a rather deeper sound. The 'smoker's voice' was so well exemplified by Lauren Bacall and Humphrey Bogart, that it is described as the 'Bacall-Bogart' sound, in books about the voice. Smoking marijuana causes the same changes to the lining and the same effect on the sound.

Alcohol has a drying effect on the larynx which is why an opera singer will not usually take any alcohol within 48 hours of a performance. It's an interpretation of the pharmacophysiology of alcohol that is perhaps exaggerated but there is little to be gained by challenging what is a long-established custom.

This view is not widely shared in rock and pop singing and the opposite is often the case. Some singers feel that some alcohol before beginning a performance steadies the nerves, and this may well be true. Some years ago an experiment was done at the Wigmore Hall with pianists who had never played there previously. Randomly, half were give beta-blockers and half were give a placebo. The jury did not know which was which and the group that took the relaxing beta-blockers scored better than the placebo group.

Travelling

The luxury days of the early twentieth century when divas travelled by ocean liner for a season at the Metropolitan or Covent Garden are long gone. Travel now is by aeroplane and, rarely, by train. Aeroplanes are dangerous places for voices. Noise comes from various sources. Not only is there engine noise but there is also the noise of the air conditioning and the airflow noise of the fuselage. This latter source of noise is around what is known as the first level of dangerous occupational noise (85 dB). If you're in first or parts of business class you will miss most of the engine noise, but in the back of the plane you are exposed to it all. The last thing that a singer therefore needs is a chatty neighbour. To carry on a conversation in a plane, you have to speak far louder than you would in a normal environment, so talking amounts to voice abuse. Now add to this the dryness of the recirculated air. The worst thing that can happen to vocal cords is to get dry. This results in microscopic damage to the lining, and constant humidification is a drill that all singers observe, knowing that full voice is not possible in a dry larynx. Fortunately this problem disappears when you get off the plane but one gig which carries great risk (as well as great rewards) for singers is Las Vegas. Singing folklore is replete with tales of singers whose voices just did not work in the totally dry desert air.

Most singers also know that alcohol is a drying agent and so will not accept the free drinks on a flight. They will bring water on board and keep drinking. Even though the water doesn't touch the vocal cords – if it did you would pour it into the lungs and drown – it keeps the body hydrated and makes up for the fluid loss that is inevitable in air travel.

Another risk of flying is getting an infection. In recent years, most airlines have stopped regularly renewing the air because it is expensive in fuel. Nowadays the air is merely recirculated. This makes passengers more at risk to any circulating bacteria and viruses from other passengers. The classic post-flight infection is with a bacteria known as mycoplasma. This causes symptoms that make you think that you're going to get a cold but it never comes to the full-blown thing. For weeks on end your daily symptoms will include a blocked nose, a sore throat, a clogged sinus or a husky voice. Each symptom might only last a day or two but the chronicity of the condition gets you down. The best antibiotic for this is clarithromycin. But the trick is knowing what you've got, and not using any of the other antibiotics.

Living in hotels

Living in a five-star hotel may be comfortable but it can be a lonely life. While appearing as a principal in an opera, a singer will work no more than three nights in a week. If they are near home then they may commute, but if they are on another continent, then the breaks between shows are too short to allow for this. There may be meetings in the theatre in the morning to iron out any problems, but generally before going to the theatre in the early evening there is not a lot to do. This is another reason for obesity formerly being an occupational hazard, because with alcohol and cigarettes off limits, food became a comfort.

Many singers keep in contact with their families using the internet. With a laptop and a small camera it's possible to see and talk to your children every day.

When things go wrong with the voice far from home, it is very worrying. And quite rightly. The voice is a singer's life and they will have a voice doctor somewhere who understands them, the business that they're in, and knows their voice and health history. If they are within a few hours flying away, I've known singers hop on a plane for a consultation with 'their' doctor rather than take a chance locally.

Climate and cultural changes

How many of you have gone to a very different climate, got off the plane, and two days later start developing a cold? I've seen this frequently in artists who come to the Edinburgh Festival in August from a temperature of say 27 degrees and find Edinburgh shivering with the temperature at 12 degrees.

They may rehearse in unheated halls, their noses are running and their throats are sore and they would rather be at home. They may have caught an infection on the plane, but climate itself can affect the respiratory tract.

When you get a viral infection, the virus doesn't die or go away to somewhere else – it stays with you and 'goes to sleep'. Although you can catch an infection from a virus that you haven't got immunity to and develop a new illness, the usual way you get ill from viruses is for one of your own to 'wake up'. One of the things that wakes them up is severe climate change.

Most viral conditions are short-lived and self-limiting but the cold continues because of something else: secondary infection by bacteria – which are very different from viruses. This happens because virus infection stops the production of an antibody that protects all your surface linings, called immunoglobulin A, and is the reason you can normally resist bacteria in a public place where they are constantly circulating. If however you have a virus infection, the production of immunoglobulin A stops, and any passing bacteria can set up house. That is when antibiotics are needed.

As a prophylaxis against this I advise singers to take an antibiotic immediately they feel the symptoms of a cold coming on; this does not 'cure' the cold but it stops it lingering, with very damaging catarrhal symptoms.

On the Indian subcontinent singers have to take care with food, because the western intestinal tract has perhaps never before been exposed to some of the entero viruses in food that would not normally trouble a local. My custom in the Indian subcontinent is to become vegetarian, which is no great hardship because that is what most of the population are. Even in the best of hotels, meat is cooked in the early morning when the heat is bearable and then reheated at night. Bad things can happen to cooked meat on hot days!

I never eat uncooked vegetables or salads, and peel all fruit. And I only drink from bottles that I have opened myself. Even then I've succumbed to gastro-intestinal disasters but I always carry an antibiotic called ciprofloxacin which is specific for entero viruses in that part of the world. Some advocate taking one of these a day as a prophylaxis but I don't do that, on the basis that I wouldn't know what to do if the diarrhoea and vomiting started!

Travelling to malaria zones means taking antimalarials. The correct ones for each region must be taken and these may be found from either the internet or a local infectious disease department.

Sleep

Sleep is about quality, not quantity.

We are all familiar with the mornings when we wake after what seems to have been eight hours' sleep and yet we feel we've never been to bed. On the other hand there are days when we feel totally

145

refreshed after only four hours' sleep. It's due to the way your brain sleeps.

The best sleep is when your brain shows slow wave activity (delta activity). The quicker the waves, the lighter the sleep, and the less refreshed we feel.

We are all aware of the effect of jetlag. When you change a time zone it takes one day for every hour of time change for your brain clock, the pineal body, to adjust. Long journeys prior to a performance need to be planned with that in mind. For a night-time performer, going east is easier than going west because they are 'awake' in the wee small hours and will be able to perform without tiredness and sleep in until lunchtime the next day.

Going west, or coming home from the east, might need some help from melatonin. This works in 15 per cent of people, but it is not just a case of pill popping and then off to sleep. It's a way of training the pineal to change ahead of time. For three days before travelling west you have to take melatonin at the time you would be going to bed at the place you're travelling to. If you're performing during these three days then there's a problem because melatonin has a slight hypnotic quality and the performance will definitely be below par.

Allergies

Allergies are usually familial and are classed into four types.

The commonest is Type 1 and means that if you are exposed to the substance that you are allergic to then that substance (the allergen) will react with the antibodies in your tissues. The combination of allergen and antibody ruptures cells that are normally present in the body called *mast cells*. These contain histamine and a number of similar substances. When these chemicals are liberated into the tissues a number of things happen. Muscles in the area go into spasm and fluid is released into tissue. So in hay fever, for example, the eyes swell with the excess fluid and the nose blocks and runs. In asthma the breathing tubes narrow and there is wheezing and a cough.

In a true food allergy (such as shellfish or peanuts) the amount of histamine released may be so great that the whole of the breathing system blocks and death results.

146

The treatment of asthma is now very successful with the many steroid inhalers. For singers however this is a problem because inhaled steroids do two things. Firstly if the user does not gargle after each use, there may be secondary infection with the fungus candida. This causes bad hoarseness. The other effect is to weaken the fine muscles of the cords (myositis) so that proper tensions for singing cannot be maintained. If this happens the steroid inhalers have to be exchanged for other medications.

Allergic chest problems can occur in a more subtle way and take a singer who is travelling by surprise. Your immune system may be able to deal with a small dose of an allergen that you are exposed to and in that case you notice no symptoms. If there is heavy pollution however, the lining of the nose and lungs becomes more porous and more of the allergen may pass into your body and set up an allergic reaction such as mild asthma or a chronic cough that may well be brought on by singing. If this happens to a visiting singer I usually put them onto a short, sharp course of steroids by mouth which will get them through their local performances without causing any side-effects.

Another type of allergy is called Type 3. It is not as sudden in its effects as a Type 1 allergic process, and is often very difficult to diagnose. It's best considered as a food intolerance. People can get vague gastro-intestinal symptoms from food products that create this chain of reactions. It is often difficult to identify the offending product because it will be generic, such as wheat or dairy products, and appear in many foods. A common feature of these intolerances are that they are worse after alcohol, which often suggests to the sufferer that they should stop drinking – but the symptoms continue. This is because in the same way that pollution makes the respiratory lining more porous, so, too, does alcohol make the gastric lining more porous to allergens and so more enter the system. The cure is in identifying the product and thereafter avoiding it.

Reflux

Reflux is what almost everyone has suffered at one time or another. It is reflux of acid from the stomach coming up the gullet and it may or may not cause the burning sensation known as 'heartburn'. If acid runs up the gullet when you are lying flat in bed at night, then it can bathe the back of the larynx causing it to swell and making your voice sound hoarse.

There can hardly be any singer in the United States who is not, or has not been, on *anti-reflux therapy*. Debates at conferences, between British and American voice doctors on this topic usually have the fur flying. Each side genuinely thinks that the other side is 'nuts'. In the USA, many symptoms are ascribed to reflux. The diagnostic criteria of our American colleagues is the finding of redness at the back of the larynx in patients who may or may not complain of reflux of acid or heartburn. They prescribe drugs such as omeprazole and if the singer improves (as they may have done anyway with time) then they stay on it for ever. If they don't improve then the dose is doubled!

In the UK we do not make the diagnosis unless there is a complaint of heartburn, evidence of reflux of gastric contents into the gullet on X-ray, and confirmation of acid in the upper oesophagus by pH monitoring – slightly more scientific – but is it any more correct? After all, many homeopathic treatments 'work' but have no scientific basis.

There is no doubt that reflux is an occupational hazard in singers because of late-night eating and going to sleep before food has been completely digested. Rather than taking a long-term drug however, it's better to alter lifestyle and eating habits. If that doesn't work then the condition should be investigated to see whether or not the singer has the bacteria called Helicobacter pylori. This is now accepted as the main cause of excess acid production and ulcers. Formerly, stomachs were removed and various nerves were cut to cure ulcers. Now if you have this bacteria you'll be cured with three weeks of antibiotic therapy.

Getting fat

If there's one characteristic of opera singers that comes to mind in the public eye, it's obesity. Although the well-known phrase, 'it ain't over till the fat lady sings' applied to an American election rather than opera, we all know that it is apt – at least until recently. Nowadays, female singers have taken on the 'image message' and it is rare that one sees an operatic heroine who is very overweight looking unlike anyone about to die from tuberculosis.

Obesity is not just associated with opera. Gospel and blues music have had their fair share of fat, mainly African-American, women.

There is no single cause of obesity. It's the result of a complex mixture of genetics, energy intake and output, and insulin behaviour. Researchers concentrate on *their* thing and so often there is an impression that obesity is due to *one* thing.

The genetic part of obesity is due to the 'ob gene' that is found in adipose tissue. If you have this you are predisposed to obesity. Present research shows that this gene stops you producing a chemical called lectin. When lectin reaches the hypothalamus in the brain you get a sensation of fullness and lose your appetite.

The energy theory is based on the equation 'energy in greater than energy out – result: obesity'. Exercise uses a disappointingly small number of calories. Drink a pint of beer after an hour of energetic squash and you needn't have bothered playing! Sit still in an armchair just breathing and letting your heart beat and you use up about 1,000 calories. Spend your day loading stone slabs onto trucks and you'll use about 4,000 calories.

We don't know if taking exercise increases what is called the *basal metabolic rate* or if you just burn off a few calories during the period of exercise. We also don't know if there is truth in the fact that the basal metabolic rate decreases to fit the amount of food you take in. What we do know however is that exercise does not form a major part of singers' lives!

The downside of just eating less than you are using is that weight loss takes a long time. To lose 0.5 kg you have to be 7,000 calories in deficit after a week's diet. So imagine that you're a reasonably active young person using about 3,000 calories a day, you'd lose 0.5 kg after a week on a 2,000-calorie diet!

Then we have insulin, a hormone produced by the pancreas. If you don't produce enough you get diabetes and have to take replacement insulin either by injection or by mouth. People vary in their insulin response to food. Some produce very little insulin when they eat. They're the lucky 'bean poles' who never get fat and are never ravenously hungry. Some produce a lot. Two things then happen. When the insulin is high, the carbohydrate you've eaten is laid down as fat. Then when the insulin falls it overshoots and goes to such a low level that you get hungry and have to eat again. This is why some people start 'grazing' after a meal; they are not only laying down fat but are taking on board unwanted extra calories.

149

Opera singers do not have thin singers as role models, nor is there any pressure to be thin – it's always been acceptable to be overweight. But now that theatre is such an important part of opera, a singer has to look at the roles that their voice is suited for and try to achieve the appropriate body shape. Excess weight on the stage has a number of serious effects on the voice.

Firstly, it's hot in the big costumes. Fat people sweat more. The more you sweat the more fluid you lose and every singer knows the disastrous effect that any dryness has on the voice. Secondly, movement is difficult to carry out realistically, especially for a theatre-minded director. And thirdly, there has to be a lot of extra effort to raise the chest when breathing in, and there is also loss of perfect control when allowing the column of air to escape in a controlled manner from the lungs. This is because all the weight of the abdominal fat pushes the diaphragm up and the weight on the outside of the chest wall pushes it in. It is best for fat singers to perform standing up, as the abdominal fat does not press on the diaphragm. When they lie down then the abdominal contents push the diaphragm up.

Getting old

We don't know why some people get old quicker than others. Ask any geriatrician and they will tell you that, like many other health issues, you should choose your grandparents well! That is the sort of useless advice that my profession specialises in, but it's true. You can do very little about your ageing process.

We don't know why people of the same age look different. Take a group photograph at a reunion when everyone is 65. Although the chronological age is the same for everyone, some will look ten years younger and some ten years older. The same spread of quality of function will range across all their senses. Some will hear better than others and some will see less well. Some joints will work as they did 30 years previously and some won't work at all without help. Some important issues are not abusing your heart with obesity, your lungs with smoke or your lower limb joints with activities that stress them.

The two things that both male and female singers will worry about towards the end of a career are appearance and the stamina and quality of the voice. Appearance can be improved by exercise. It has been clearly shown that people over 60 will enhance not only their cardio-respiratory condition but their whole being with weightlifting. Muscle is about the only tissue that it is still possible to improve and build on as you get older. The obvious alternative way to look better is by cosmetic surgery.

If you want to improve an ageing face consider a face lift, blepharoplasty (eye lift), botox and cosmetic dentistry. It's all expensive and you must choose your surgeon or dentist well. Fortunately, since the Bristol heart surgery case and the Harold Shipman case, the medical profession has been much better controlled. Unfortunately, it is still possible to fall into the hands of 'cowboy' cosmetic surgeons, but the risk is much less than before. If you have a limited budget, the best small procedure to reanimate the face is an upper lid blepharoplasty. It can be done as a daycase procedure and is 99.9 per cent successful in making you look better.

Changes in the voice due to age cannot be improved by surgery! If the singer has an excellent technique then they will be able to go on longer. As you get older, the central nervous system starts to disintegrate and control of muscle is lost. So the less you have to do in the way of compensating for poor muscle technique the longer you'll go on.

The place where technique, or the lack of it, shows, is in the passagio. Pavarotti undoubtedly has the best technique heard today and this is why he is still singing superbly even though he is almost 70. The Italian idol that he replaced, Guiseppe di Stefano, finished singing at 39 because his passagio technique was poor. He, like Russell Watson, Mario Lanza and other 'popular' tenors, enters the passagio not around D or E, but at F or even G. This gives an enormous excitement and flair to the D and E sung with a high chest voice but it is not a technique that will allow singing into old age.

What happens to the nervous system with age is the same as happens to the rest of the body. It starts to wear out. There are fewer nerve cells in the brain and this is one of the reasons why old people are almost never travel sick. There's not enough left to be confused by the movement to allow the impulses spill over into the cell nuclei and make you sick and pale.

There are fewer nerve fibres to conduct electrical impulses to and from the periphery such as limbs, ears and eyes. This is why you don't react as you once did to a tennis ball coming over a net or a ball being thrown or kicked to you.

The basic structure stays but there's less of it and it goes slower.

Muscles also start disappearing. They never actually disappear but their mass gets less. There are fewer motor units and so the muscles get fatigued earlier than they used to. In the larynx therefore, this means that the mass of the thyro arytenoid gets less and so the fundamental frequency of the larynx may rise a little. One of the vocal curses of old age is that women's voices tend to lower because of submucosal deposition of oedema fluid, and men's voices tend to rise because of loss of muscle mass.

Adjusting to these changes often leads to muscle fatigue problems in all grades of singer but especially the elderly amateur. It is usually manifest in the production of an uncontrollable wobble which signifies an uneven recruitment of motor units. The regular recruitment is represented by a narrow and regular vibrato. A wobble is a vibrato of uneven amplitude and frequency. The wider the amplitude, the worse it sounds. Former admirers of Carreras now find it sad to listen to what happens to his vibrato when he sings loudly.

15

Recording Techniques

When you listen to a voice you enjoy hearing a beautiful sound, a catchy melody, an interesting rhythm and meaningful lyrics. When a singer sings a song, they enjoy the experience, the buzz of 'going public' to possibly millions of people, and the joy of performing. But the people behind it all, who make it all possible, want your money. They'll get your money from the tickets you buy for the theatre or the concert, from the merchandise that might go along with a particular company, group or singer, but mostly they hope you'll buy the records.

This chapter is about how records are made.

Benefits of recording

When you consider that the entire works of a composer like Bach disappeared for the best part of 150 years till 'rediscovered' by Mendelssohn, it gives an appreciation of the enormous archival benefit of recording music. We might never have known of Bach.

Recording has also had a catalytic effect on the music industry and has opened up to both composers and artists an earning potential that was beyond the wildest dreams of Mozart, Beethoven and Schubert. It has also brought music to millions of listeners who otherwise would have had no access to it.

My grandfather was an opera lover. He lived in Edinburgh, and died in 1940. He got enormous enjoyment from his huge collection of 78 rpm records, not only of arias, but also whole operas that sometimes took 40 sides to play, with the record deteriorating with every play. He would happily sing along with Caruso, Gigli, Chaliapin and De Reske. He had books that told the stories of all the main operas and listed the recommended 78 rpm recordings. And yet he had probably never seen an opera live. If it hadn't been for his records, a whole world that he enjoyed would have been denied him.

In 2002, we read of an enormous recording deal between EMI and Robbie Williams. Exactly 100 years previously, an even better deal was struck. The late Fred Gainsburg, of The Gramophone & Typewriter Company, against the orders of his bosses, paid Caruso the then enormous sum of £100 to record ten songs. This was accomplished in an afternoon. Over the next two decades Caruso made nearly £1 million – and the industry, £2 million! This initial record was made on a wax cylinder, and this is how it was done.

Wax cylinders

The first recording machine was made in France a year before Edison got his patent in the USA. The basic construction was a diaphragm, connected to a stylus, which in turn cut a groove in a rotating cylinder of wax. This created a waveform of sound against time. If you then reversed this, the grooves in the wax cylinder made the needle move, and signals were sent back to the diaphragm, which moved.

The reason that the early companies, like HMV, mostly recorded voice was that it was far easier to record than an orchestra. The singer could stand next to the diaphragm and literally shout at it to get the stylus moving on the wax. In the original Berliner gramophone, the sound from the diaphragm was amplified by the horn, which, with a dog looking into it, became the logo of HMV for over a century.

Before records came along, no one knew what their voice sounded like. This was an acute problem for singers, because prior to recording, they had only ever heard their own voice by what is called bone conduction, which was through the bones of the skull to the inner ear. When they heard a recording of their voice, they heard it for the first time as other people did, which was through the ear canal. The first records therefore sounded strange to singers, because people had to get used to a rather different sound from that which they heard every day.

Because of the technology, only singers with bright voices, that is those who had a 'ring' at 3 kHz, could reproduce well. Thus, tenors and female singers were the first recording artists. One of the major problems with this method was that you couldn't make a master. Until this technical problem was solved the singer had to sing into the horn for each record. There was obviously going to be no commercial future in this, and so after a lot of research, the horn was connected to several wax cylinders.

The next major advance was when the wax cylinder became a flat disc and the stylus did not need to be heated. The wax however was so soft that you couldn't press anything on it to make copies or else the grooves would distort and the recording would be lost.

This problem was solved when they discovered that spraying copper onto the wax to put a 'plating' on the back stopped it bending and distorting. They now had a master disc from which hundreds of copies could be made by pressing soft discs on to the hard surface so that the grooves would imprint. These are now the discs that are given as gold, silver and platinum awards to artists who sell the required number.

78 rpm records

The invention of shellac allowed 78 rpm records to be mass produced. Shellac was a forerunner of plastics and is a Bakelite material in-filled with slate powder to cut down wear. It goes soft when heated and hardens at room temperature.

The early 78 rpm records were made with what is known as the 'hill and dale' method, a description that comes from the depth of the grooves – the deeper the groove the higher the intensity. It was impossible to edit these records, and so recordings had to be 'right' before the session could end. Only tunes that lasted about three minutes could be accommodated on one side of a 10-inch 78 rpm. When they invented bigger 12-inch 78 discs then up to five minutes was possible.

With the advent of the Berliner flat disc, the lateral groove method was introduced. The needle went from side to side as the intensity varied, and this method was used right through to the introduction of LPs. If you lift a 78 rpm record and slant it into the light, you can see the loud and soft passages from the different reflection on

155

the narrow and wide grooves. The industry did in fact make use of this to check equipment and set up the disc cutter for the required tone. A Bechmann Meyer image was created by shining a light across the record. The light is proportional to the velocity of the cutting stylus and this in turn is related to the intensity.

These discs had a limited shelf life because they were 'damaged' with every play. Basically, you used one of three types of needle. The *Thorn needle* did not damage the record, gave the best sound, but only lasted 1 or 2 playings. The *medium soft* lasted about 30 playings, but as it got older it would become blunter and damage the record. The *hardened steel needle* lasted over 100 playings but eventually damaged the record.

Tape recording

The era of the theoretical 'perfect recording' arrived when the tape recorder was invented. The reason for this was that, for the first time, editing was possible. It was done by literally cutting pieces out of the tape and splicing them, so that there was a seamless join. It meant that during a recording session, several 'takes' of the song could be recorded and the best 'take' edited and improved by insertion of better bits from other tracks. For example, if a tenor performing Rodolfo from *La Bohème* could not get the high C in performance, then the poor high C would be cut out and a high C which was recorded at another time as a single note would be inserted.

For more than 20 years, tapes competed against vinyl records and consumers usually had a choice of formats. With the increasing in-car entertainment systems and the introduction of Walkmans, tapes became very popular because of their versatility. With the advent of CDs, however, and the modification of personal stereo equipment to handle CDs, there was no longer a place for tape recording in the music market. On the other hand, it still remains the basis of recording prior to processing and distribution. The main difference now is that digital systems rather than analogue are used for even simpler editing.

Long-playing records

At about the same time as tape recorders became widely available, a new material, vinyl, was brought into use. At the same time, Decca brought in microgrooves, calling them 'full frequency range recordings' (FFRR). Because the groove was smaller, it could be cut with greater accuracy, and there was less background noise because of the chemistry of the material. It also meant that the singer did not need to sing so loudly in the recording studio because a lesser intensity could be given a wider dynamic range.

Two things allowed LPs to actually play for longer periods. Firstly, reproduction was possible at slower speeds (33 rpm) and secondly, since the grooves were smaller in depth and width, there were more of them. They were cut with a heated sapphire stylus that created a groove by softening the vinyl.

Another type of LP which rotated at 45 rpm was smaller and was convenient for pop music. This was because, at that time, a 30-minute recording did not suit the pop music of the era. Each side had a couple of tracks, and because they were recorded at a faster speed, since they were not required to last for more than 10 minutes a side, they could be recorded with much less expensive equipment. Although they were introduced for the pop market they also proved a suitable vehicle to introduce a completely new audience to classical music. A number of companies marketed series that included popular overtures, movements from symphonies and famous arias, and these really did capture the imagination of a public that would never before have considered even listening to 'the classics'.

By and large these records were played on portable equipment with 2.5-watt amplifiers, small speakers and cheap turntables. The louder the sound that was in the recording, the less electronics were needed in the equipment. The recording process was therefore tailored for maximum noise from minimal equipment.

Stereo recording

The next development was stereo and this was a huge theoretical advance especially for classical music. With directional ambience you could get nearer to the concert hall sound.

The basis of stereo is a right and left channel corresponding to right and left ears. There are right and left microphones for recording, right and left amplifier channels and right and left loudspeakers. It was also very easy to record stereo on tape because the recording head had two sections and the tape had two tracks.

Also, there was a fundamental change in the recording process. Records until now had kept to the hill and dale method with the needle going from side to side in the groove as loudness changed. In stereo records there is still a groove but the needle does not merely run in the base of that groove. There are two needles in stereo equipment that lie at 45 degrees to each other and pick up from either the left or the right wall of the groove. What now represented the intensity of recorded sound was not the depth or breadth of the groove, but the angles of the walls of the groove. The louder the noise the bigger the angle the walls made with the base.

Stereo recording not only made a huge difference to the replay of classical music but it had an even bigger effect on cinema sound.

Analogue recording

This was the method of recording that was used up until the invention of the fast microprocessor that powers modern computers. Before we go on to the technology of modern digital recording, it's of interest to look back at the methods that 'made' the music industry.

Analogue recording stored a signal that varied in proportion to the loudness received by a microphone. Since the signal accurately reflected the amplitude, the quality was prey to inadvertent noise and distortion from things like noisy amplifiers. In an analogue recording a singer creates a sound pressure wave that passes the microphone at the speed of sound (1,100 fps), making the diaphragm in the microphone vibrate according to the variation in air pressure caused by the sound. This creates a low-level voltage which varies by exactly the same amount as the sound pressure wave. This voltage then passes to the tape recorder where a magnetic field is radiated by the recording head. This field is varied by the low voltage signal and is 'memorised' as the tape passes the head at 15 inches per second. Running the magnetised tape past a replay head at the same speed recreates the original voltage which accurately represents the original sound signal. This is then amplified to a level suitable to drive a loudspeaker to recreate the original vocal sound.

In the analogue recording studio, there had to be careful adjustment of the tape recorders and a good quality of tape had to be used to get good quality results. Editing an analogue tape involved cutting and splicing tape segments.

Digital recording

Unlike analogue recording, digital recording does not pick up the sound pressure variations as voltage changes, but converts the sound pressure changes into numbers, which represent the amplitude of the signal. Thus in numerical form, the signal is immune from distortion and the noise that is inherent in any electrical processing. A number such as 3,456 will be passed through the electronic system with no risk that it will, somewhere along the line, become 3,458, which is the equivalent of what happens to an analogue signal.

It will be immediately obvious that something special has to happen to the speed of uptake if even a simple signal such as a singer singing a fast scale is to be converted into numbers for each note change. The sound from the microphone is measured every 44 thousandth of a second and appears as a stream of numbers. The sampling must not only be fast enough to catch the frequency changes but must be fast enough for the listener not to hear the reproduced sound as a broken up sequence of samples.

Anything that can be changed into numbers can be stored in a computer. A CD recording uses 44,100 samples of information for each second of music. Each of these samples is turned into 16 numbers and, since it has to be heard in stereo, they are doubled. If you consider that a single song will last at least 3 minutes that means that almost eight million pieces of information have to be imprinted. MP3 technology (MP3 stands for Moving Picture Experts Group audio Layer 3!) allows this information to be compressed, by removing the seldom heard parts of a recording, and this allows quick downloading from song files held in other places.

If these numbers are then converted back, at an identical rate, and the signal used to drive a loudspeaker, then the original sound will be heard.

Once the signal is stored in numeric form it can be kept in a computer memory like any other data and can then be mathematically processed to achieve many special effects which would have been quite impossible with an analogue sound signal.

Editing digital recordings is accomplished by a process very similar to word processing. Press a number or a key on a keyboard and sound segments can be changed with absolute accuracy.

Compact discs and DVDs

CDs are made from the master tape which was recorded digitally. The transfer of the data from the tape to the CD surface only requires to satisfy binary levels of 0 and 1. This is achieved by using a laser to burn pits in an optically reflective spiral track on the CD. Each pit represents a logical 1, and no pit represents a logical 0. The numbers are stored onto a CD and these numbers are recovered at the sampling speed of 44,100 samples per second and converted back into an analogue signal. The original sound will then be heard.

The reason that CDs can hold so much information and can play music for over 65 minutes is that the grooves are enormously long because they are so close. If you straightened out the grooves on a CD they would extend for 3 miles!

CDs are now the commonest means of distributing music, but technology is going so fast that they are liable to be supplanted at any time. Since sound can be stored digitally on CD, DVD and MP3 it may be transmitted across a computer network.

This is the cause of the present serious threat that is now facing the recording industry and which has caused the present slump in sales. Music is not only readily available from the internet but the recording mediums are no longer subject to destruction when playing, like the original 78s.

A DVD works in exactly the same way as a CD but it can hold a lot more information – about 4.7 gigabytes, which is about seven times as much as a CD. They can hold more because the bumps are smaller and the tracks closer together giving them more storage space. The typical contents of a movie stored on a DVD are 133 minutes of high resolution video at 720 dots of horizontal resolution, a sound track presented in up to 8 languages using 5.1 channel Dolby digital sound and subtitles in up to 32 languages.

They will also store almost eight hours of music.

In 2002, Apple launched the first digital music player, the iPod, which is likely to do to CDs, what they once did to vinyl records. At the same time Apple created iTunes, which allows you to plug your computer into the internet and download music legally. The previous similar devices recorded and stored digital music files by means of an electronic memory, but iPod uses a small hard disc. Basically it is a hand-held jukebox that can hold up to 10,000 songs in a compressed format, a process that was made possible by MP3 technology. The compression however means some loss of quality but they are not meant to be a substitute for a HiFi system, more a means of living and travelling with your own 'soundtrack'.

Recording environments

In the past, classical recordings were not usually done in studios because the sound is 'dead'. Great concert halls, such as the Henry Wood Hall in London, were in almost constant use for recording orchestral or instrumental pieces.

To be of any use for recording, a hall has to have *resonance*. Every object, and almost every place, has a resonance, but it is the timing and type of that resonance that is important. If we had a place with absolutely no resonance, firstly it would have to be built specially for sound experiments and would be called an anechoic chamber, and secondly it would have such an odd environment that you would not even hear a gun make a bang – it would only make a click!

The ideal recording hall has to be shaped so that resonances between walls, ceilings and floors are avoided as far as possible. The worst sort of hall is one with parallel surfaces that build up specific resonances at inappropriate frequencies. A hall with a straight overhanging balcony is unsuitable for recording because the distances from the sound are the same and the sound is not broken up. The curved balcony of the old fashioned Victorian theatre is quite good because the distance from the sound source varies and so modern halls, such as San Francisco, Glasgow and Cardiff, with balconies at different levels, have good acoustics. Some halls put acoustic panels on the roof that can be tilted to stop inappropriate resonances by making the surface irregular.

161

Before the cascade of electronic technology brought today's sophisticated tools, a sound engineer would do a simple test to see if a hall was suitable. He or she merely clapped their hands and ideally wanted the sound to go on for about five seconds. The target reverberation time is one second for the voice and five seconds for instruments. An aircraft hangar, for example, would be of little use because the reverberation time might be as much as ten seconds. A cathedral also has a long reverberation time and thus is good for choral music and slow sermons. Cathedrals are of no use for solo singers or fast speech!

When making a recording, the sound engineers set up the microphones. A whole orchestra can be recorded with as few as three. A stereo pair are put where the listening head would be. They represent the two ears, and are panned, when, for example, the sound moves in one direction. Some parts of the orchestra may need augmentation, and so one or two wandering microphones will be moved about at different times as required.

Nowadays, studios are being used more frequently than halls, because all the effects can be added later. The sound however still has an artificial quality. Good quick reverberation is needed for the voice and for classical orchestral or instrumental music. Nearly all instruments used in classical music need reverberation to make them sound 'normal'. Playing in a studio makes them sound hard and brittle. On the other hand, studio recording is preferred for big swing bands and also pop music because they don't want any natural reverberation. These both need a 'dead' background so that effects can be added later in mixing, and reproduced at whatever wattage is required through powerful speakers.

This is why live music sounds better and why you are persuaded to part with money for tickets.

16

Marketing the Voice

Opera as we now know it in the UK has developed greatly in the last 60 years, but since 1990 it has become one of the most popular art forms. Most people of all ages and tastes could name two or three opera singers. In some ways we are now catching up with most other European countries, where opera has been *the* art form for centuries.

There were two main reasons why the UK was a latecomer to opera. The first was that almost no operas of note were written with an English libretto, and so, without surtitles, it was difficult to do anything other than appreciate the music, the voices, the sets and the costumes; understanding the production was difficult or impossible.

The second reason was that there was a long tradition of choral societies with the large choirs from places like Huddersfield, Bolton, Sheffield and Glasgow doing four or five major concerts a year along with great singers such as Clara Butt.

At the end of World War II, Sadler's Wells came back to London and the Royal Opera House was set up at Covent Garden in 1946. Now there are virtually no big choral societies left because aspiring professional singers have so many routes not only into opera, but musical theatre and pop.

Few people realise the size and complexity of an opera company and how a season is planned and paid for. The singers are what everyone thinks of but it needs an army of people to create and manage a season.

Planning an opera season

For a normal season, preparations should ideally begin two years ahead of time, but due to recurrent uncertainties of Arts Council support this is not always possible. If a major production such as *The Ring* is being planned then preparations have to begin more than three years ahead because there are only a limited number of singers who have suitable voices and you have to get half a dozen top Wagnerian singers booked years ahead.

The repertoire for a normal season is selected to present a balance of old favourites, resurrected classics and perhaps (if the company are feeling rich!) a modern work. The selection is made by the musical director, the director of planning, the chief executive and the board who are responsible for setting the budget. Typically they will choose six operas that will play in their major theatre(s) and some of these will go on tour.

The first person to be appointed for each opera is a director, because he/she is the key to the opera's success and thus the choice is critical. Since there are so few excellent ones, there may be difficulty with timing and availability. Because the choice is so crucial, the decision is taken at the highest level, by the same people who take responsibility for the repertoire.

Baritone Sherrill Milnes divided directors into two. The first was the traditional one, who did their homework and came along to rehearsals knowing exactly what was required. The second type had 'flair' but knew little about opera. Such directors may start by saying 'Let me hear the music and then I'll decide how we do it'! The director has a big say in choosing the rest of the team such as directors for sets, costumes and lighting.

Opera in the UK has been theatre-based since the end of World War II, and in the last 50 years there have been three major figures. The first was Carl Ebert who worked at Glyndebourne from the Forties to the Seventies. Every director of note for that period was a trainee of Ebert's. People like Anthony Bosch and John Cox continued to transmit the method to another generation.

The next one was Zefferelli, whose life story was so brilliantly fantasised in the film *Tea with Mussolini*. His production of *Don Carlos* at Covent Garden in 1958 was a landmark and a turning point. Finally there was Feldstein, who had the luxury of working in post-war East Germany with endless resources. He was a textbook socialist realist, would rehearse for eight months, and if he didn't like it, he would cancel. He looked for every detail in the most realistic fashion. His disciples were Harry Kupfer and Joachim Hertz in the Seventies. He once said 'We know what Wagner wrote but we don't know what he dreamed'.

Choosing the singers

Directors of Planning will have an encyclopaedic knowledge of singers wherever they may be. They spend a large part of their time attending operatic performances all over the world and also visiting the main music academies. In these days of limited budgets for provincial companies, Scandinavia and eastern Europe are happy hunting grounds for British Planning Directors.

They will hear every final-year student in the UK, and the interesting ones will have a private audition. From this, the company will develop a list of which singers would suit specific productions in the future. The director has to be involved in selection along with the music and planning directors, because his production may well require acting skills that are beyond the skills of the chosen singer.

Established singers are usually booked up to two years ahead. Ideally, nowadays, they should look the part, sound the part and be able to bring to the part any special skills that are required. Not least, for a provincial company, they have to be affordable! They have to be able to sing in the required language. English, Italian, German or French seldom produce problems for professional singers. Most are conversant with Czech and tend to sing it phonetically, so if you understand Czech, you will understand more of a Czech libretto than one in another language.

Putting it together

The timetable for preparation is worked backwards from the date set for the first performance. The first day of rehearsals will be six to eight weeks before the opening. Three months before that, the sets are approved and costed. Models of the sets are made, including furniture and people. Three months before that, the technical team will present ideas for design, materials, architecture and costumes. The lighting director will be involved all the way through because set design will have to accommodate special lighting effects.

Once the plan for the season is completed, a weekly 'Call Sheet' is prepared and posted every Friday. This tells everyone – singers, musicians, covers, coaches, designers, repetiteurs, conductors, orchestra, directors – where to be, at what time and for how long.

The head of music is responsible for a very underestimated and virtually unknown job in opera, namely that of the repetiteurs. These are a very special group of people who train specifically for the job. Every year a few places are kept at the National Opera Studio for their training. No one ever hears of them and they never get curtain calls. They however, are the people who do all the hard work in preparing the singers for the performance. They will be top class pianists who are excellent sight readers. They will play for all the early rehearsals, which is very difficult because they not only have to play complex scores that have been cut down from the orchestral score, but also they must watch the conductor. When not playing for rehearsal they coach the singers individually, to help them understand how the conductor wants the music styled. They don't coach in either voice or language. The language coaches are freelance and operate separately as opposed to the repetiteurs who are mostly salaried. In the old European opera houses they were called 'dramaturgs' and they sat out in the audience expecting to hear every syllable.

Rehearsals

The timing of these depends on the complexity of the opera, the production and the singers. For a well-known traditional production of something like *La Bohème* or *Carmen*, four to six weeks will be enough, but for a new production of a Wagner opera more than eight weeks may be needed. Rehearsals start in the music room with just the singers, the conductor and a repetiteur.

The next phase is the 'Sitzprobe' meaning 'seated rehearsal'. This will be the first time that the orchestra and singers work together. The shape and sounds of the vowels will be practised, as will the timing of the climaxes and the shape of the quiet passages. The dynamics of duets, trios and quartets will be sorted out so that one singer does not unbalance the sound and the choristers will be positioned so that the naturally louder voices are in the right place at the right time.

They then go to the theatre for stage and piano rehearsals and these are led by the director because by now the conductor will have instructed the cast to produce the music as he wants it. The sets are in place and the singers wear costumes, wigs and make-up. The lighting director is there and modifications are made. Sets may have to be modified if they interfere with the acoustic and resonance of the voices. If they are staggered and the stage is big there will be some positions from which the voice is 'baffled' and inaudible. The ideal sets for singers are flat, because sound bounces off them towards the audience. The problem is that they may appear uninteresting.

As the budget for set design becomes more limited as well as the cost of storage, so lighting has become a much more important component of an operatic production.

The pre-general rehearsal is four days before the opening night and it is the first time that the opera is run straight through. The dress rehearsal is the day before.

The economics of opera

If you wanted to make a fortune you would not run an opera company. The economics of it do not make sense, but opera companies have to be supported because of the immeasurable cultural contribution that they make to society. Opera companies cannot survive as businesses as understood by bankers and financiers. Indeed, without regular transfusions of money, opera could not survive at all.

Apart from the Royal Opera House at Covent Garden there are five main opera companies in the UK – the ENO, Welsh Opera, Opera North, Scottish Opera and Glyndebourne. Each has a payroll of several hundred, employing both the orchestra and the chorus on a full-time, salaried basis. They are all structured appropriately for any company running budgets of this size.

No opera company can pay the salaries and productions from box office takings alone. Even an opera that consistently fills every seat in the house, such as *Carmen* in English, could never cover the costs in a major theatre. Normally, UK companies make 10 per cent from the ticket sales, achieve 20–30 per cent from sponsorship and require 60–70 per cent from Arts Council Grants.

Most of the European opera houses sell tickets in the £15–70 range. One or two are well in excess of this, such as Royal Opera House (£160), the Metropolitan in New York (£280), and the Vienna State Opera (£190). Covent Garden gets £20 million (about 28 per cent of its budget) from the Arts Council. It has to find the rest from corporate or individual donors. Opera is fortunate in having a major benefactor in the Cuban American billionaire, Alberto Vilar. He has donated hundreds of millions of dollars to opera houses throughout the world in the last few years, including New York's Metropolitan, La Scala Milan, Covent Garden, Los Angeles Opera (where Domingo is the artistic director) and the Mariinsky Theatre in St Petersburg. But the money is quickly swallowed up, with each production costing between a quarter and half a million pounds to stage, and famous singers like Pavarotti, Domingo, Cecilia Bartoli or Angela Gheorghiu getting paid in the order of £15–20,000 per performance.

Opera houses all over the world are feeling the draught at the moment, not only due to the downturn in the financial markets but to a reassessment by governments of the perceived value of high cost productions being paid for by taxpayers. It is doubtful if even the city of Berlin will be able to continue to run three opera companies as it has done since the Fifties. Opera Australia has trimmed its plans, and the troubles of the ENO, Scottish Opera and Covent Garden are never far from the newspaper headlines in this country. Last year Scottish Opera were refused any government help to recover from debt and had to disband their chorus.

We are a long way from the golden age of wealth and subsidy supporting opera. Once, the famous director of the Salzburg Festival, Herbert von Karajan, was asked what he would do if one of his productions was looking like running over budget. He replied, 'I call Vienna and the government sends more money!'

Until recently the most comfortable place in which to run an opera company was Germany where the grants are from the regional, not the national arts councils; these cover approximately 90 per cent of requirements. While artists are paid a little less and taxed far higher, the ticket prices are also lower and opera is available to a larger cross-section of society. In Germany the musicians and singers are on the same payroll as the bus conductors and municipal workers, but it's a very secure job. It used to be like this in Italy but grants have been severely cut back and the dozen or so companies are contracting. The season now in Milan, Naples and Rome lasts a fraction of the time it formerly did when Italy was the opera capital of the world. The productions of the old favourite operas now play to packed open air audiences in venues such as the Arena at Verona and the Villa Borghese in Rome.

In the USA the financing is even more precarious. There is only one full-time major company and that is the Metropolitan of New York. Opera in America depends solely on ticket sales and private sponsorship. There are no government or municipal grants but the tax laws make sponsorship more attractive than in Europe.

The ENO has several full-time principals, but other companies outside London have difficulty in achieving this. One of the dilemmas which are becoming a source of conflict in all the UK national opera companies is whether it is necessary for an opera company to carry a large salaried orchestra and chorus. The opponents of the policy say that this is an extravagance preserved by the unions and bankrolled by the taxpayer through the various arts councils. They argue that all these people are not required permanently on the payroll because no two operas are the same in their requirements for chorus or orchestra numbers. Some need no chorus, some need men choristers and not women, some need dancers, some need no brass instruments, some need ten French Horns, etc. They argue that it would be more realistic to function with a small nucleus of an orchestra and a chorus, and to hire in freelancers on short-term contracts to suit the planned repertoire. In this way you would not have to pay people to do nothing. The counter argument however is that the savings would be minimal, and the quality of performance would suffer, with knock-on effects at the box office.

Some companies however basically do just this. Glyndebourne, for example, hires a new chorus each year and hires either the London Philharmonic Orchestra for grand opera, or the Orchestra of the Age of Enlightenment for eighteenth-century repertoire.

The outstanding success of Mr Raymond Gubbay was often quoted as a reason for cutting down on permanent staff. He receives no public subsidy, and yet puts on successful operas in huge venues such as the Royal Albert Hall and Wembley Arena. But he also does not use top flight principals and all of the operas are sound enhanced. To a wide audience this is how they are used to hearing the recorded voice and so to them sound enhancement is no bad thing. It is, however, totally alien to the traditional opera lover. Unfortunately, when Mr Gubbay tried to apply this principle to the production of regular operas in a small venue it failed.

While some houses, like the Met, will coyly admit to 'some sound enhancement', opera should not be performed with the directly miked voice that one hears in music theatre. The music for opera was not written with the amplified voice in mind and the technique used by opera singers is not really suitable.

Basically it's a trade-off between quality and cost. If an audience wants the balance of a well-rehearsed orchestra and a perfectly projected unamplified voice then there is a limit to the size of venue. The biggest opera house will seldom seat more than 2,500–3,000 and so the box office take is virtually capped. If, however, you use a venue that holds three or four times as many people then you may well cover the costs – but the quality of the traditional operatic sound will be altered because of the necessity to use amplification.

Selling opera records

The classical music record market is saturated. You need a very good reason to produce another cycle of Beethoven symphonies. On the other hand, singers are all different, even if the accompaniment is the same, so some market still remains for them. The leader in classical music record sales for the last fifteen years has been vocal music. It started in 1990 with the football World Cup in Italy. One of the English football commentators, who was a classical music buff, persuaded the BBC to commission Pavarotti to sing 'Nessum Dorma' as the signature tune. The Three Tenors concert, with Pavarotti, Domingo and Carreras followed, and that album sold 12 million copies. Although all three singers are very wealthy men they must be regretting that the company, Decca, paid them a one-off fee and they did not get any royalties!

The second concert in Los Angeles in 1994 was seen by a TV audience of 1.5 billion throughout the world. From that time onwards, 60–70 per cent of the best selling classical records have been in vocal music, either opera, Lieder, selections, crossover, collations or cleaned up recordings from the past.

170

This is a huge change. Thirty years ago you could walk down any high street in Britain and ask people who the conductor of the London Symphony Orchestra was. Ninety per cent of people would have been able to tell you that it was Andre Previn. Now, hardly anyone would know. In other words, singers have displaced conductors.

There are a number of other reasons for this. The age of 'the great conductor' has passed. At the moment we have Simon Rattle, Claudio Abbado and Christopher Dohnanyi but there are no 'giants' such as von Karajan, Toscanini, Beecham or Furtwangler.

Today opera records are sold in two ways. The first is through the so called majors, such as HMV and Virgin, and the second is through the independents, such as Opera Rara. Things are now getting much tighter, and the 'good' days for the record industry are in abeyance. While the availability of downloads from the internet has affected classical sales, it has not had such an effect on this market as it has had in the pop field. The main reason is that the 'classical' market has run its course, and a new angle on marketing is required to push it forwards.

Companies have tried shining the searchlight on to baritones such as Bryn Terfel, since the public may have had enough of tenors, but this is not a long-term solution.

It is only thanks to the success of crossover singers such as Russell Watson or Andrea Bocelli, who have a small foot in opera and the other in middle of the road pop, that Decca are able to fund new opera productions at all.

Recording a whole opera for a boxed set is very expensive. For a Wagner or Puccini opera the orchestra might be over 100 and they all require union rates. Top recording artists such as Pavarotti or Cecilia Bartoli might take a 30 per cent royalty from the dealer price of a recording, which is the cost to the store before their profit is added on, and this makes the road to profitability a very long one. Furthermore, many opera lovers will be happy with a mid-price recording of the same work by stars of earlier decades.

Opera Rara on the other hand, funded by the Peter Moores Foundation, have unique selling points. Their chief executive, Patric Schmid, has an unrivalled collection of Rossini, Bellini and Donezetti scores, along with almost unknown operas of composers such as Meyer, Payer and Pacini. The music is catchy and singable and the cast is built around the famous tenor Bruce Ford. They use the

171

St Martin-in-the-Fields orchestra (on the basis that they cost the same as the others but are so expert at reading and interpreting that the recording gets done quicker). The same applies to their regular chorus of the Geoffrey Mitchell Singers. This is a niche market that does not have the competition faced by 'yet another' recording of *Aida*.

Similarly, the EMI Debut series gives young artists the chance of getting known. They have perhaps been prize winners either at college or in competitions, they are well thought of, and will have done a Wigmore Hall recital.

Because of the draughts blowing through the record market at the moment, contracts are changing. A record company would once upon a time offer an artist a five-year contract and in that time expect them to produce three or four CDs. The contract would mean that the artist can only record with that company for that period. Conditions varied. Some artists took a fee for the period, some are on a percentage and some get sessional fees.

As in all the arts, the people who turned down the future stars such as The Beatles are remembered. The A&R man at Decca who turned down Charlotte Church was fired, even though he had discovered Barbara Bonney, Rene Fleming and Andreas Scholl! When Charlotte Church was 12 she was given a contract for five CDs and each sold more than a million. Records by Bryn Terfel always sell, as do those by Ian Bostridge. The latter singer however does hardly any opera but he sells more records than regular operatic performers because of 'marketing' by the majors. Similarly, records by Andrea Bocelli and Russell Watson sell well, even though they are sometimes cruelly known as 'circus acts' within the profession of singing. Andrea Bocelli is blind and hardly ever appears in opera for obvious reasons, and Russell Watson is a tenor who handles the passagio with an incorrect technique, which sounds very exciting today but will probably not stand the test of time. They sell well because they have 'personalities' and can be marketed, and their record producer has advised well on the repertoire, which is crossover and has something for everyone.

Setting up a West End musical

For the past 40 years the West End of London theatres have been the centre of musical theatre. This is largely due to the talents of Andrew Lloyd Webber, Tim Rice and Cameron Mackintosh. They have had the vision and the not inconsiderable courage to back shows that at their inception may have been hits or flops.

The first thing that a composer of a new show will look for is a producer. There will be no show without money up front and so the search starts for investors or, as they used to be called, 'angels'. Unlike opera there is no government subsidy unless a show is put on at the National Theatre. The investor's money sinks or swims on what happens next.

The producer will recruit a choreographer, a writer, a stage director, a design director for sets and costumes, a musical director and a lighting director. The next step is casting the principals and finally the ensemble. Auditions for the ensemble will attract hundreds of young hopefuls. They will get a short initial audition and much will depend on their appearance.

Once the cast is in place rehearsals will begin. As previously explained, because everything has to be paid for there is never time for more than four weeks' rehearsal. The cast move between dance, stage and singing rehearsals under the different directors. If there is a lot of movement in the show then ankle and knee injuries are inevitable and so understudies from the ensemble will also have to rehearse different roles. All in all the rehearsal time for a musical is far more intense than the rehearsal phase of an operatic production.

The music is composer- rather than conductor-led. A principal artist may get a relatively free hand if she or he is the first person doing the part, but if she or he is following a principal who has made the part well-known and successful then their performance has to be an absolute copy. In many ways the final product is like a blended whisky. Each year a blend may be made of an entirely different mixture of malts and grains but the end product has to taste the same every year.

Elaine Paige told me that she took the part of Evita after Julie Covington had made the record popular. Andrew Lloyd Webber wanted her to sing it in precisely the same way as Julie Covington had sung it, even though Elaine thought she could improve on it in many different ways. On the other hand, when she opened *Sunset*

Boulevard in the role of Norma Desmond she had a much freer hand because there was no 'known product' that had to be imitated.

Selling music theatre and film music

Tim Rice and Andrew Lloyd Webber were masters at marketing. As long ago as the Seventies they devised the plan of popularising a hit song from a show that had never been seen. The song 'Don't Cry for me Argentina' was in the charts long before the show Evita was on the stage. And so, with so many other good songs, was it surprising that the album sold?

This was the technique used for all their musicals and it worked. The format was always the same. A disc that runs between 50 and 60 minutes that has all the major songs on it sells for full price. If a show runs for years, new people are going to see it every night and so there is never any need to discount.

The music from the musical theatre is not as novel and popular as it used to be. There are a number of reasons for this. Firstly there are no truly great musicals on in the West End just now. People are scratching around with nostalgic rehashes of Abba, Queen and Buddy Holly, and the well-worn pattern of the Lloyd Webber-Rice format. Also the attempt to 'jazz up' the West End stage with soap stars who can't sing has failed.

Film music has largely taken its place. When a film is made nowadays, one eye is kept on this part of the merchandise market. Usually there is enough music in the background for a CD, and you are often astonished that the blurr of sound you heard in a film like *Lord of the Rings* actually represented about a dozen songs, each with an individual title!

Some films such as *Sleepless in Seattle*, *When Harry met Sally* and *As Good as it Gets*, unashamedly used well-worn standards as the soundtrack and these were certain to sell.

Economics of popular music

For many people, recorded music is their first choice for entertainment, and almost 90 per cent of all records feature the voice, in either solo or group form. So with an eager customer base, all a company needs to do is to get enough people to buy *their* record; it should be easy because millions of people buy records every week.

However, if it were so easy there would have been no need to dream up programmes like *Pop Idol* and *Fame Academy*, or to manufacture groups for specific markets. It is a mass market business and sales must be developed, not only nationally, but universally. This creates huge production and promotion costs and perhaps up to a quarter of a million records have to be sold to break even. The stakes are high. If a company has a hit, then the profits are in millions, but one flop can also lose them a million dollars.

Let's take the hypothetical situation of a local group that wants to expand. They write a song, they record it and play it around clubs. Their manager gets an A&R man interested. He then persuades his employer, let's say Universal Music, to sign them.

The group will perhaps be paid £150,000 and be told to make their first album in 6 months and another one in another six months. These contracts will be processed by the company law department who negotiate contracts with the artists, their manager and their producers and agents. The money paid up front to the group is however only a form of loan. The amount is offset against future anticipated sales. Sometimes a group will make no more money until their third or even fourth album. Ever since the 127-page judgment resulting from the case that Sir Elton John brought against his former manager Dick James, it is harder for companies to defraud artists.

The main song will be given to a publisher, who will start trying to get it radio plays or put into an advert. The publisher will deal with the Performing Rights Society so that the group can get money for whatever plays are arranged. Remember it's the songwriter, not the artists who gets the money from the publisher.

When the group have written more songs and have recorded their album in the very best studio conditions, the company may press a quarter of a million CDs. While this is going on, the head of merchandising directs the art department to render sketches and have photographs done. The copy is written, the graphics are assembled, and a cover emerges.

They will then turn attention to POP (industry shorthand for 'point of purchase') stimuli, and these will include posters, banners, stand-ups, special display racks, window displays, and perhaps souvenir items that the retailer can give away to shoppers. Once the CDs are pressed and the cover is done, they will pass to the marketing division who will arrange storage, delivery and distribution of the album to retailers such as HMV or Virgin, big bookshops like Borders, and supermarkets.

At this stage, marketing will activate the musical press through their press department and they will place interviews and features in the appropriate newspapers and magazines. At the same time they will arrange radio plays, perhaps a video and club promotions. If strong word of mouth develops through dance clubs and the record is getting good air play on the radio, then the album may be heading for the charts. The group's agent will be working with concert promoters to get additional exposure through tours and concerts.

Once the public start buying the album, what happens next depends on its performance in the charts. In November 1952, *New Musical Express* published the first UK *singles* chart on the basis of telephoning a selection of record stores; the number 1 in the first chart was Al Martino singing 'Here in My Heart'. The first UK *album* chart appeared six years later when South Pacific was the best seller.

When *Top of the Pops* was first broadcast in January 1964, presented by Jimmy Saville, the Beatles had six records in the Top Twenty, with '*I Want to Hold Your Hand*' as number 1.

Almost 20 years later, Gallup took over from the British Market Research Bureau and automated the data collection. This is basically how it is done today, with data coming from 5,600 high street retail outlets and 600 independent stores covering 99 per cent of the singles market, 95 per cent of albums and 80 per cent of videos. The chart run-down at 4pm on Sundays is still the most listened to programme on BBC Radio 1, and the UK charts are regarded as the most reliable in the world.

Selling pop records

This is the hub of the music business and whole books have been written on this subject alone. This section will try to simplify it.

The previous section profiled the people involved in the creation of an album. But there are even more.

As previously explained A&R people are the scouts the record company. They spend a lot of time listening to new groups and travelling the country. Their decisions and skills are based on subjective taste, public taste, the fashion curve, the market and the media. They decide where the company should invest and that ultimately decides the fate of that label. Once they have signed a new artist they will create a relationship with them and their manager. They will decide the budget for the recording of an album and will decide on producers and studios. The cost of a studio can vary from £100 a day to £3,000 a day depending on facilities, reputation and how busy the studio is at the time.

Once an album is made, the promotion and press people have to create interest, and the manufacturer must find a way of getting it to potential customers at the right time and in sufficient quantities. There has to be a national network of distributors to get the product to the retail outlets such as Virgin and HMV. Small labels cannot do this.

Price wars among retailers have a direct effect on distributors, and there is a constant appeal for better discounting. Major record companies handle distribution through the branch offices of their affiliated distribution companies. These offices usually have two divisions. One handles regional promotion and the other concerns itself with distribution and sales.

The merchandising of records is the largest segment of the music business. As well as normal distributors there are 'rack jobbers'. A customer walking into the record department of a major store cannot know just by looking around whether the record selling area is a department of the store, a space leased to an outside company, or whether it is serviced by a 'jobber' who supplies the racks and the bins. They operate particularly in supermarkets and locate the record racks near the checkout. They display just the current popular discs and this helps foster the charts because only those that are designated to be hits will actually turn out as hits because the charts work on the sales.

Performing rights, radio and TV

Music is everywhere around us; in concert, festivals, radio, TV, shopping centres, lifts, clubs, pubs and discos. All music is created and owned by someone and they have a right to be paid for it.

177

Music users (clubs, shops, media etc.) would find it impossible to get permission to play the music of hundreds of publishers if they had to seek permission on an individual basis. Instead they pay a fee to the Performing Rights Society and may then play any music that they wish, but have to report it to the PRS who also have inspectors who do random sampling. The size of their fee depends on the venue size. Pubs, for example, pay according to their average number of customers. Although it is a huge operation, only 5 per cent of song owners get more than £10,000 a year and 85 per cent get less than £250.

When a new album is issued, the press department will set about their work. They will set up magazine and TV interviews with the artist, and people called radio pluggers will see that the tracks are played on Radio 1. They will not deal directly with the DJ, but with the head of play listing at the BBC. Contrary to popular belief, most DJs do not choose their own records. They go into work and play from a list prepared for them by the head of playlists. As you might expect there is a lot of 'wining and dining' at this stage.

If a track is played on Radio 1, it is heard by a large number of people in the UK because it is the national music channel and has by far the biggest audience, both active and passive. The next biggest is Radio 2 and below this is regional radio. The best times to be played are between 5 and 9 am, after 6 pm and all weekend. Outside these times the audience is much smaller.

When a new album has been made and is about to be issued, people called 'pluggers' will make sure that it is played several times a day at the end of the week, and the press team will insert interviews and articles in the magazine that is appropriate for the age group that the record is aimed at. On the Sunday and the Monday the artist will do TV interviews, and when the record is released on the Monday it will sell upwards of 2,500 on the first day. After *Pop Idol*, the Gareth Gates album sold over a million on the first day. At £15 an album, that makes the artist and songwriters millionaires in a day.

17

Developments in Voice Technology

In the previous chapters I've tried to show how the popular singing voice has changed to reflect current tastes. The early church voice, the troubadour, the declamatory Grecian dramatic style that led to opera, and the pragmatism that led society to deflect religious rules by castrating little boys for vocal beauty have all been major changes in vocal usage. While the nineteenth century development of *bel canto* technique has laid the foundation for modern operatic style, the rise of American culture has formed the present day theatre voice with the accent, the twang and the belt.

It is doubtful if there will be any more such major changes in singing style that do not depend on technology. We saw what an important effect on singing style the development of the microphone and amplification had; it started a completely new era of popular music. So how is voice technology going to develop and how will it be used?

In the twenty-first century, money rules. People cost money, and so any technology that can replace people is worth developing and using. In the field of voice we have many telephone answering systems 'which will be recorded for training purposes and your protection, because your call is valuable to us'. Like most people I usually end these experiences in a rage, but you have to admire the technology of speech synthesis which gets better every year even though the words remain inane. The technology of voice recognition is not making as many secretaries and typists redundant as was at first feared but that day will also come. Here's how it's done.

Speech synthesis

Speech can be synthesised after a huge database of phonemes has been established from the human voice. These are stored in digital form after spoken words have been cut up into the various phonemes. In the English language there are between 40 and 46 phonemes depending on the regional accent. There is a different set of phonemes in every language. Some languages such as Cantonese depend on change of tone of a single vowel to impart change in meaning. The creation of synthesised speech in tonal languages is done in the same manner but there are more possible combinations.

A matrix of the 40 or so phonemes is created and in the simplest form of synthesis, *diphone synthesis*, parts of phonemes are joined together depending on the word. For example if you synthesised the word *sad* from *s*, *a* and *d*, it would sound like a child reading phonetically. If the word is synthesised from the matrix then the later bit of the *s* is added not to the whole *a* sound but just to the earlier part of the sound; this produces the sound *sa*, and the *d* is added on. Even then it gives a very unnatural effect and many will have heard it when Stephen Hawkins 'speaks'.

The second way is called *unit concatenation synthesis*. This uses a much bigger database of phonemes and puts them in a contextual setting. For example you can change the pitch of the word depending on its place in the sentence or its relation to the word of origin, as well as the type of reading material. For example an automated weather forecast might say '*Today it will rain in London*' while the automated sports service might say '*Arsenal beat Chelsea today*'. The way *today* is said would be different in both sentences while in the simpler *diphone synthesis* it would sound the same.

When the database is set up an operator can type in whatever they want the computer to 'say'. It is thus very good for automated weather forecasts, news headlines, and sports services. Orange, the mobile phone firm, already has a service whereby you can phone in and have your emails read to you by synthesised speech.

In situations where responses are simple, common and predictable, then synthesised speech can be used even with the personal touch added. Through speech recognition your voice can be recognised and the synthesised speech will address you personally. Telephone banking is a good example of this.

Everyone is driven mad by telephone software that leads you

through the keypad before you can get to talk to someone. At the moment this is done by recorded speech (so called *canned speech*), but it could be done by synthesised speech with a personal touch.

The sad thing about all of this is that the public perception of communication is being altered. We are doing away with one of the basic things that makes us human. We used to write letters and then we made phone calls. Now people are liable to send seven emails rather than talk on the telephone. Just as some soap operas led to a change in accent and phrasing by some sections of society, so synthesised speech is causing many people to imitate the sound and movement of synthesised speech.

Speech recognition

Speech recognition is the technology which converts the spoken word into a command for a machine to understand. The commonest form is the widely available computer software that allows rudimentary dictation to be converted to text documents.

Perfect and 100 per cent reliable speech recognition will probably never be accomplished, largely because human beings are not 100 per cent reliable when it comes to spoken communication. In fact many humans can't be understood by other humans who speak the same language! The variables are daunting – language, dialect and phrasing will be different from speaker to speaker. Speech recognition packages require to be trained by an individual speaker by reading a given text. From this the software builds up its own phoneme base for that individual. Phonemes are the sounds that we collect together in different sequences to form speech. For example the word '*sounds*' is made up of one syllable and four phonemes, namely, '*s*', '*ou*', '*n*' and '*dz*'. Similarly the word *alphabet* has three syllables and six phonemes namely '*a*', '*l*', '*f*', '*b*', '*e*', and '*t*'. The word *glass* has four phonemes in English and five in a Belfast accent, *galass*. The computer memorises the tens of thousands of phonemes that an individual uses and puts them together as words depending on their sequence. Minor variations of these will in the early stages confuse the computer and so many corrections will need to be made, and it is at this stage most people go back to typing! Not only is the package sound sensitive, it is also context sensitive and so it may create a series of errors depending on what it identifies as the context of what is being dictated.

At a simpler level the technology works much more reliably. Lights in a home may be switched on and off by speech command as may telephone systems in cars. People can play chess simply by stating their moves. Fighter pilots who have their hands full can instruct their armament to fire. There is of course potential risk of serious error if the keyword such as '*fire*' is accidentally uttered. Speech recognition must be context sensitive in many applications. Disabled people may also control machinery and a similar technology may one day be transferred to everyday life so that it may become possible to get into your car and say '*Take me to Bognor Regis please*'.

Forensic speech recognition is still at the stage of being a 'black art'. If an analyst was presented with two studio recordings containing the same words, they could tell if they were made by one or two people from the patterns in the words, the speed of closure of the velum (palate), the speed of the tongue on a vowel and by the spectral analysis. When speech recognition is forensically important however, the material is from a telephone recording or covert surveillance recording. There is rarely enough material to get the above information separated from background noise.

Teaching of singing

When singing teachers visit our labs they are very impressed with the 'bells and whistles' but I've often wondered what it will do to teaching methods when all the technology becomes more widely available. If I had to put money on a long-term bet, I'd wager that music teachers will do what they always did in regard to teaching voice production – use their ears and experience. The availability of video laryngoscopy and stroboscopy to see the cords vibrate in slow motion, laryngography to show whether or not the cords are vibrating efficiently and spectography to show whether the resonance is good, are going to be enormously helpful adjuvants to good teachers but will never replace knowledge, ear and experience. It is likely that traditional methods by experienced teachers will always achieve the best results. However the scientific information may help to weed out dangerous teaching methods and overcome specific problems.

The art of singing involves many layers of activity ranging from voice use to performance. The achievements of a singing teacher are heavily psychological and motivational. The risk of less experienced teachers using the available technology is that they might invest effort on a single aspect such as vocal brightness or vocal power, which if taken to excess will ruin the all-round potential of the voice. The aim of voice training is to make the singing voice sound effortless to the audience while being as natural and effortless as possible to the singer. If a teacher concentrates on one misunderstood area of a measurement it would spoil the singer's voice. It would be like a car driver who was told to drive continuously at a certain distance from the kerb – the overall performance would be damaged. The teacher who has included scientific study of the voice in their training will be reassured if the measurements correlate closely to what they hear from the singer.

Have you ever wondered why there are still people who tune pianos manually when you can buy an electronic tuner for most other instruments? This is because tuning a piano is an art which, because of cross resonances, cannot be done by a machine. In other words there is no instrument that can reproduce the response of the human ear. So singing teachers will always exist and will be irreplaceable by any other form of learning or measurement.

Listening to the voice

In listening to classical music the acoustics of the concert hall make a huge contribution to what you hear. These acoustics are a complex combination of echoes and resonances perceived as the sound reaches the listener from all directions. Up till now classical music has been recorded in halls known to have good acoustics, such as the Henry Wood Hall in London or the former St Andrew's Hall in Glasgow.

In future they will record in studios that have very little acoustics, an environment that is known as 'dead'. Modern digital filters can mimic the sound characteristics that make up a particular resonance. The first step in doing this is for a sound engineer to fire something like a starter's pistol or a similar object that gives a short sharp 'bang', in a concert hall and then to record the result over a period of say 15 seconds to ensure that all the features of the hall echoes are captured. This is called the impulse response of the hall and by digital techniques (i.e. by changing the frequencies to numbers), an electronic filter can be designed so that it will impart the hall's acoustic feature to any music played through it. All of this is made possible by the speed of modern digital signal processing which must keep up with the real time event.

This technology is already available in very simple form in various sound packages which can be bought for your computer. You can now buy programmes that allow the selection of drawing room, church or concert hall acoustics for any sound file. In the future you will be able to buy filters that reproduce the acoustic of any famous concert hall in the world. So buy the recording which will have been made in a 'dead' studio, insert a card into your hi-fi, sit back and you will experience the sound of San Francisco, Milan or Sydney.

I showed how the introduction of usable microphones allowed amplified singing to give us all modern song forms from musical theatre to rap. I also explained why a singer should try to gather harmonics at the 3 kHz level in order to give the voice the operatic 'ring' and project it unamplified into a huge theatre. This has long been used in the recording of popular singing but it is now entering the classical field. Some American opera houses are now using what is called sound enhancement which is a system of microphones that enhance the acoustic at around 2–3 kHz. This enables singers to concentrate more on acting, and to sing with less effort. It also gets over the problem of bad acoustic design in older theatres.

Earlier in the book I said that you can't make a good voice out of a bad one, but I should have added one more word – yet! You'll remember that the teaching of the passagio was the most important part of creating a professional singer. Listeners want to hear the same quality in a voice from the bottom to the top of the range. Almost anyone can sing at least one good note. That note is sampled and used to produce a song sung merely by changing the pitch – and lo and behold it has exactly the same variation in timbre throughout the whole song!

The pop singer Cher was the first to use the technique known as *voice morphing* in one of her recordings. This is a technique where, by means of digital signal processing, all the imperfections are removed from the sung note and pitch corrected. This is now used as a stylistic tool by some pop singers and it can give an unreal quality to the human voice. Although we'll shortly see the possibilities presented by the synthesis of speech, Yamaha have already produced a tool using this technique for shy karaoke singers; sing one note and the voice synthesiser will do the rest. Will some clever producer one day find a role for this technique in making commercial recordings? I doubt it.

In this book I've described about fifteen hundred years of voice production and the only technology that has altered singing has been the microphone and amplification. Even that is too much for opera lovers but it did create a completely new genre of popular and theatre singing.

It's a fool who ever says 'that's it' but I'll be brave enough to suggest that if there is another 'it', I won't be around to hear it.

Index

A&R men 121, 172
ageing 120, 150–152
alcohol 120, 142, 143, 147
allergy 146–7
air travel 107, 143
American accent 55, 118
amplification 50, 65, 91
analogue recording 158

backing singers 58
baritone 38–40, 55, 104–6, 171
bass 38, 106
basso profundo 39
belting 55
beta-blockers 142
birdsong 25
boy trebles 89, 113

camerata 76–77
canons 73
castration 80–86
cat purr 28
cathedral choirs 112–113
church singing 71–73
chorus, opera 104
Colleges of Music 99–100
compact discs 160
continuum, voice 32
contralto 35, 66
counter tenor 57, 87–89
Country and Western 69
crooning 55, 68, 94
cysts 131–2

digital recording 159
dog bark 27–28
DVDs 160
dystonias 136–7

ear 4–5

'Fach' system 103
falsetto 57
film music 174
functional aphonia 136

giraffe 28–29
glandular fever 133
Gospel 66
granulomas 131

harmonics 7, 8, 18, 33, 41, 42, 44
hyaluronic acid 33, 39

infections 128, 143, 144–5
intubation 131

jazz 66, 117

laryngograms 17–18, 41
laryngoscopy 130–132
larynx
    ageing effects 15
    cricothyroid muscle 13, 88
    functions 2, 5
    ligaments 10, 34, 43
    motor units 20–21

187

larynx (*continued*)
  muscles 10, 19
  myotatic reflex 21
  nerve supply 13, 29, 126
  puberty 15
  sex differences 2, 14
  shape 2
  skeleton 9
  supraglottis 12–13, 45
Lieder 59, 111–12
long–playing records 157
lungs 13, 22–23

'Machinests' 75
manufactured pop 122–23
mezzo soprano 35, 66, 104–6
microphones 91–93
Minnesingers 74
minor salivary glands 128
misuse injury 99–100, 126
musical brain 40
music theatre 53, 118–121, 173–4

Napster 97
National opera studio 102
nodules 128–130
non-voiced singing 57

obesity 144, 148–50
opera directors 164–5
opera, economics 167–170
Opera Rara 36, 171
operetta 53
overuse injury 99–100, 126

passagio 47–49, 151
Performing Arts Medicine 141
Performing Rights Society 175, 178
polyps 131
pop, economics 174–8
pop voices 64, 117
post graduate programmes 101
presence filter 64

rap 97

recording, hill and dale 155
recording, lateral groove 155
recording studios 161–2
reflux 147–8
rehearsals 119, 166–7
repetiteurs 102, 167
resonance 4, 6, 7, 8, 12, 33, 44, 45
rock 'n' roll 95–97

Scuola Cantorum 73
seventy eight rpm records 155
'Sitzprobe' 166
sleep 145–6
soprano 34, 46, 57, 104–6, 113
spectrogram 46, 60, 68, 90
speech recognition 181–2
speech synthesis 180
stereo recording 157–8
stroboscopy 42–43, 127, 130
syrinx 26

tape recording 156
teaching 100, 114–16, 182–3
tenors 36–39, 104–6, 113, 170
thyroidectomy 134
tonsillectomy 135
troubadors 74
twanging 56, 69

UK charts 176

vibrato 50–51, 152
vocal cords
  component parts 11
  effect of smoking 12, 126, 142
  mucosal vibration 17, 41, 127–8
  nerve supply 13
  Reinke's space 11, 15
  thyroarytenoid muscle 11
vocal tract 45
voice morphing 184
voice types 32

wax cylinders 154–155